W9-CNP-329

A STAR BOOK

TRANSITION

A SENTIMENTAL STORY OF ONE MIND AND ONE ERA

BY
WILL DURANT

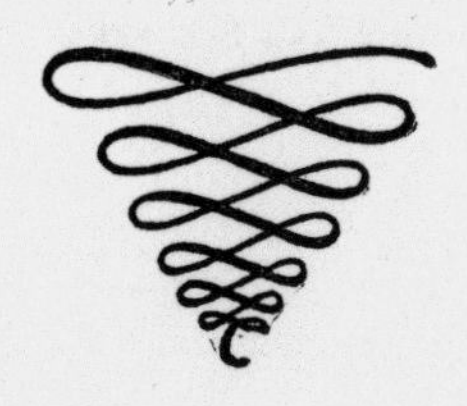

GARDEN CITY PUBLISHING COMPANY, INC.
GARDEN CITY, NEW YORK

PRINTED IN THE UNITED STATES OF AMERICA
AT THE COUNTRY LIFE PRESS
GARDEN CITY, NEW YORK

To a

Tender Mother

and a

Perfect Father

FOREWORD

DEAR READER:

Perhaps this is your story as well as John Lemaire's. It tries to show the effect, upon one growing mind, of the profound transformation which modern science and research have brought in the faith of the western world. In a lesser way it tries also to show the political experiments and disillusionment of our time, and to trace the evolution of a fairly typical rebel from Utopian aspiration through a cynical despondency to some measure of reconciliation and good cheer.

These changes have not been as impersonal as the abstract chronicle of history represents them; they have brought to sensitive individuals much suffering in mental transition and readjustment; they have broken up families and friendships; and they have unsettled the mind and morals of many generations by uprooting the customs and beliefs in which those generations grew. It is with this personal aspect of the Great Change that the story is concerned.

WILL DURANT

Sea Cliff, May, 1927.

CONTENTS

PART ONE: THE GREAT CHANGE

PART TWO: THE NEW WORLD

CONTENTS

PART ONE
THE GREAT CHANGE

CHAPTER I

I LOSE MY INNOCENCE

My earliest memory pictures me held up high in the hands of a rough but kindly Italian, and searching for candy in the pockets of his coat, that hung upon the wall. I was always a hearty eater, and perhaps it is a little symbolical that this vivid operation of the primal instinct is all that I see when I reach back as far as I can into my childhood years. Apparently this Italian lived with our family; at least I yet see him, across these pitilessly moving years, coming in at the close of the day, and hanging his coat and hat upon his individual nail. Sometimes there were peanuts in the coat, sometimes candy, sometimes popcorn, sometimes nothing; and then my benefactor would not lift me up as usual, but would soothe me by bouncing me on his knee. He was a handsome fellow, as almost every Italian is; and though his coat shone with time and work, I loved him with what my memory describes as a mute and ardent affection. It is strange that I remember him so clearly, and yet have no vision at all of how my mother or father, or any of my brothers or sisters, looked in those early days. But some remembrance is his least due; for I am sure that his gruff bestowal upon me of part of his unused fund of paternal tenderness taught me, almost in my swaddling clothes, the genial kindliness that lies in the hearts of men.

We lived, it seems, in a little town called Readsboro, in Vermont. Already, in 1885, it was industrial. I remember it as whitened with the dust of pumice or cement mills, and inhabited by simple laborers who had long since abandoned the effort to keep clean. They worked hard, probably twelve hours a day; but they were a jolly crew nevertheless, and had energy enough after their toil for games and brawls that made the place no paradise for philosophers. On Saturdays and Sundays the square in front of our house was animated with baseball; all the noise that makes amateur sport so much more exhilarating than the calm routine of professional games, filled the streets and poured in at doors and windows and echoed to the limits of the town. Sometimes the ball would follow the noise; once it crashed through a window and fell almost at my feet. We were not greatly astonished; we could put in a pane of glass ourselves in those days, and we knew that in these hilarious ceremonies America expressed one element of its spontaneous religion. The other element was in the factories.

Yet these blunt and hearty men, who fed the machines in the mills, exchanged hospitalities in the saloons, settled various national and sexual problems in their street-corner conferences, and retired at last to their homes, their sporting-sections, and their pipes,—these men and their wives, though they constituted nearly all the population of the town, were hardly accorded the name American by the bent and wrinkled farmers who clung with timorous piety to the ancestral hinterland. To the sons of the Puritans these factory-workers were "Polocks," "Guineas," "Micks," "Sheenies," and "Canucks"; they belonged to strange and presumably inferior peoples who had chosen America as the cesspool for their waste. The farmers, encrusted in thirty years of dirt, looked with stern disapproval upon these workers dusted over with the pumice of the mills, heard with horror their score of dialects, and wondered what America was coming to. They saw their fields turned into factory yards, their streams poisoned with chemicals, their clear skies darkened with smoke, themselves unnoticed and displaced. Even they knew the tragedy of transition.

I think I can recall—or am I reading between the lines of my memory?—a fundamental difference between these farmers and the later immigrants who filled the town. The farmers looked tired and worried and unhappy; the factory workers looked strong and self-confident, and were always ready with smile and jest. The isolation of the farmers had made them unsocial; the deterioration of the soil had led to the exhaustion of their energy; the hardness of their lives had embittered them to all the world; and their religion was sterner and crueler than life itself. But those men who passed our house after the whistle blew, or filled the square on holidays, had a strange exuberance, a freshness of spirit as of people who had found renewed youth. In the midst of exploitation and hardship they remembered the stagnant misery of their native shores; and of an evening they would sit content on their steps, smoking the pipe of peace, trading stories with their neighbors, and listening with the calm of nicotine as their sturdy wives retailed to them the accumulated gossip of the day. Beyond these ruined farms they saw the promised land; and though they knew they had but seen its portals, they nursed the silent hope that their children would enter the kingdom.

They were a believing generation. They believed that in this endless expanse called America there was a road for every talent to rise to wealth and power. They frowned upon the employer who worked them ruthlessly; but they scorned with superior pride the young orator or the pallid student who suggested that they take over these factories and send members of their own class to rule the cities and the states. They found a secret zest in this gamble of the individualistic life; they were aware that most of them would lose; but as long as they did not know just who would win, they wished the game to go on. Its uncertainty was its lure.

And they believed in God. They never doubted that He was seated somewhere in that cloudy sky, surrounded with myriads of angels, and watching with paternal affection the fortunes of these queer crea-

somest of them all, dark and proud and silent; perhaps more like his father than any of us—and I could yield him no finer compliment. I was a little jealous of his good looks, but I admired him humbly, and prayed that I might some day be as clever and handsome as he. After me came Ben, whose big head is still pictured in the memory I have of the time when I rocked his cradle, and who was to be, of all the family, my one unflinching friend in the days of my tragedy. And finally, two incomparably pretty young sisters, of whom, as still within the blushing age, I must say no more until they cross the current of my history.

The Reader will perceive that I have described our little family as almost perfect. He will understand that we all had our vices and absurdities, but he will not expect me to advertise them while we have still so many years (I hope) to live in this rude world. And he will smile at the way in which I shall make myself the center of this circle; it will be ridiculously unhistorical, for certainly each one of us placed the core of the world's affairs in his own heart, and only by literary license may I presume, henceforth, to focus the story upon myself. If these brothers and sisters had the "gift of gab" and were, like me, heavers of wind and hewers of words, what a different story they might tell!

We boys managed to live in a fairly moderate degree of warfare, considering that we were brothers. Many mad ventures we had together—many more, no doubt, than our memories have had room to hold. I recall one as particularly impressive to me, because it introduced me to sin, and gave me the new and awful experience of breaking one of the ten commandments.

We had all gone to play near the river that ran beside the town; attracted partly by our mother's standing prohibition against treading those slippery banks, and partly by the procession of logs that floated downstream from the forest to the mill. Leo and Fred, bare-legged, waded in with that timid audacity which blooms in us when we know that we are observed. Some of the logs drifted so near the bank that the boys caught them, and had great fun in rolling them about. At last the idea occurred to Fred and Leo to stand with one foot on one log and the other foot on another. So for a while they towered like brave Colossi, while I, too young for this achievement, pranced on the bank in admiring ecstasy.

Then one log took a mind to roll over, and Fred plunged up to his neck into the water. Leo was so disturbed by this turn of events that his own footing slipped and he joined Fred in his involuntary bath. I shouted with fright, but they commanded me to hold my peace. They found their way to the shore, shivered a while, and then conferred on the problem of keeping this log-rolling business from our mother. With youthful decision they made a fire, undressed, and tried to dry their clothes over the flames. However, as supper-time was at hand, and to be late would invite questioning, Leo and Fred got into their clothes before the drying was quite complete, trusting that the journey home would finish the process. But suddenly it came to them that I might blurt out the whole story.

"Listen, Johnny," said Leo, "you won't tell on us, will you?"

"Oh, I won't tell on you," I said, like a man of four big years.

"If ma asks where we've been we'll say we were looking for berries."

"All right."

"And whatever we say, you say the same thing—understand?"

I tried to understand, though I was a little frightened at this multiple mendacity. I had lied before, but it had been natural, instinctive lying, not lying aforethought as now. My mother had told me how awful it was to lie, and how if I died just after a lie I would go to Hell and never see the face of Jesus. I trembled a little, but probably less than Fred and Leo, who feared no such distant and purely hypothetical punishment. Nevertheless we screwed our courage to the sticking point, and marched into the house as unanimous in falsehood as Lord Melbourne's Cabinet.

The questions were asked, and Fred and Leo lied like statesmen. My turn came, and I did my best, gulping down my theology and reciting my terrible untruths with an exaggerated positivity. I mourn to think that my unnatural insistence on what should have been offered as obvious and unworthy of emphasis may have aroused the suspicions of my mother. At all events, she spied the limp sag of Leo's shirt and Freddie's trousers; she felt them and sniffed them,—and the game was up. Then there was weeping and gnashing of teeth, and the fire of discord was not extinguished until we were all of us tossing in troubled sleep.

My mother looked at me sadly the next day. I am absurd enough to think that before Ben and the younger girls grew up I was her favorite, and my immoralities hurt her more than those of the hardened sinners who had been favorites before me. That dear mother of ours was bound to make a saint of one of us, and tried her best to inoculate me with every virtue. To think that after all her love and all her lessons and all her prayers I should stand up and lie to her like a young Lucifer—this was hard to bear. I am afraid there was some doubt about my sainthood in the little mother's heart as she cared for her brood that day.

CHAPTER II

I PUT ON PANTS AND BECOME A SAINT

HOWEVER, even a terrible thing like a lie can be forgotten, especially if other troubles succeed it. The time was coming soon when I was to make my début at school. I was not to be five till November; but the parochial school might accept me in September if I came in the proper moral and physical condition. The physical condition meant that my face and neck should be washed, my hair brushed back from my eyes, my shoes shined, and my legs clad in holeless stockings; while the rest of me was to be covered with pants, and a pretty blouse with a great stiff collar that fell over my shoulders, and a flowing tie that hung down on my breast. It was a tremendous experience to be so thoroughly accoutred; and I pleaded successfully with a fond mother to let me practice in the new equipment on the Sunday before school opened. I went to church with the pride of an alderman, said my prayers like a starched Aloysius, and came back throbbing with maturity and perfection.

Suddenly a group of boys, meeting me, burst out laughing, and called upon other boys to look at me; and when they too burst out laughing my new manhood melted into hot and helpless tears. I looked angrily about me to see the source of the laughter; but I saw nothing, and my anger grew. Then one lad pointed, and looking down I discovered that a button had come loose in the most strategic portion of my pantaloons, and a certain secret which decent lads conceal had been betrayed to the public eye. I covered up the error in mad haste, and ran home sobbing. It was no fun being a saint when one was built just like other boys.

That unseemly episode made a thinker of me. I brooded for hours, even in the midst of ball-games and walks, over the mysteries and melancholies of anatomy. Why were certain portions of me so much more sacred than others, requiring to be veiled in sanctuary from eyes that looked unhindered on my questionable nose? What were other people like? Were they all like me? What were these queer things called women? How were babies born?—I constructed for myself a marvelous system of physiology, which later life painfully brought nearer and nearer to what I now presume to be the truth. Curiosity burned like lava in me; and yet I dared not ask questions; it was sinful to be interested in such things. Perhaps, in school, when I learned to read, I might ferret out these holy secrets of human origin and female form.

And so I went to school,—with the button replaced, and a gold ring on my finger, and a heart a-flutter with the expectation of strange events. It was a Catholic school, taught by the Sisters of Charity. I was taken to the Sister Superior, and introduced as a candidate for education. However, the good Sister would not have me. She petted me and praised my blouse and approved of my trousers without suspicion of their shameful history; but she gently informed my sponsor that I was too young.

"Bring John back in February," she said, and turned away to other applicants—real, sensitive boys and girls who were watching the universe revolve about their focal selves even as you and I. And I came home defeated.

When I reached the house I found that the gold ring was gone from my finger. I quite understand that the Reader does not care about that ring; that he suspects it was only gold-plated, and not worth bothering about. But that missing ring meant tragedy for me; it brought to a suffocating climax the failures and indignities of two days which had promised to be heroic stepping-stones in my career. I swear I cared almost nothing for the ring; but my throat ached with the desire to repair at least one of the stupidities of my matriculation day. I can see myself now, over the hills and valleys of the intervening years, retracing every step that I had taken from the school, and searching every foot of the road and the path, with a heart beating and pounding as perhaps the rise and fall of nations would not make it beat again. And then when I could hardly walk any more I came home in utter humiliation, convinced that I would never amount to anything in this hostile world.

My mother was kind to me that day,—hardly scolding me, and understanding, with a word, just how my little cosmos had collapsed about me, leaving me poised in cold thin air, disconsolate.

A queer gap in my memory, and then I see myself kneeling on the floor of the classroom in the school, punished for some misdeed.

Apparently February had come, school had opened its arms to me, and perhaps, even, I had been there for a year or two; I cannot tell. But certainly I had done something villainous; for this business of kneeling was the penultimate penalty inflicted on the young criminals of that institution. It was no way to make piety palatable; but it awed us as few punishments would have done, and achieved a transient efficacy.

Now this habit my memory has (contrary to the most highly guaranteed psychology) of picking out the dark spots of my past, must not deceive the Reader. I would have him understand that I was a bright boy, led most of my classes, and in general astonished my teachers with a voracious intellectuality. If the things that I remember and record seem to stamp me as a dunce and a culprit, the Reader must take my word for it, in place of specific memories, that I was an unusually clever student, who always knew more than was good for him. Perhaps I was something of a trouble-maker, pretty nearly the worst-behaved boy at school in some of my younger years; I may decently concede that, for nobody is ashamed of misbehavior at school, except in his children. Schools are unnatural contrivances; and though we enjoyed reading and arithmetic, we hated to sit still for three hours in the morning, and then two in the afternoon, and then—for us bad boys—an hour after class. Unconsciously we longed for those ancient pedagogues who took their boys out for a walk, and taught them the nature of things not from blackboards and slates and books, but from the illuminating face of the world itself. Nothing learned from a book is of much use anyway.

Nevertheless, here I was in school. Now that I look back upon them, it seems that they must have been happy and exhilarating days. What adventures we had on the way back and forth, what lively quarrels and exciting games! I should like to record that I could "shoot marbles" with the best, and brought my marble-bag home every day a little heavier than it went forth. Even school itself had its consolations; for the very teachers that scolded me for insolence and conceit liked the way I picked up my lessons, and began to give me prizes, and told the priest what a pity it was that so good a student was so troublesome.

Meanwhile they poured religious instruction into us, and taught us many pretty prayers and sweetly sad hymns. They hoped that these lessons would mould us, however slowly, out of our natural barbarism into some measure of consideration, honor and kindness; and perhaps in most of us the seed was not planted without some pretty growths. After all, we are at birth mere animals, dirtier and uglier than the puppies in the litter; our parents alone can tolerate us (after a while), or nurses who have become hardened to the native human form. Only that great school, the family, and that great family, the school, have been able to debrutalize us, by forcing upon us the accumulated decencies of group life. If they have used, in this process, an abundant amount of legendary lore, let us remember that they believed these legends true, and thought them indispensable to the salvation of our souls. Perhaps, in an earthly sense, they were; and these marvelous myths were like milk teeth—doomed to decay on contact with the rough realities of the world, but useful until such time as stronger structures could take their place.

To me, in those impressionable years, these myths were a great delight, and filled me with awe and poetry. Indeed it was as poetry that they won us; we listened to the story of Adam and Eve in much the same mind as when we heard tell of Jack the Giant-Killer and little Cinderella. We did not ask were these stories true; they were interesting and wonderful, and that was enough. And then when the figure of Christ stepped into the legend we were thrilled as by no other story ever; here was a hero greater and nobler than any, who had been the fearless foe of tyrants and the unjust rich, who had died not for one fair woman only, but for all mankind; and who through all his adventures and his sufferings had been as beautiful as Hoffmann painted him, and as gentle as a maiden's love. We saw pictures of him, chubby and rosy in his mother's arms, standing unshaken among the learned doctors, lashing the merchants out of the Temple, feeding the multitudes, welcoming the little children to him, forgiving the fallen woman, sitting at the last supper to break bread with his betrayer; and then on the way of the cross, scourged and mocked and wearied beyond bearing, crucified between thieves, pierced with a lance, and taken down into the arms of his mother, dead. What stones we should have been not to be touched to the depths of our hearts by this noblest story ever told, this finest flower that has ever blossomed in the jungle of the human soul, this magnificent symbol of genius crucified for daring to redeem mankind!

Was it any wonder that this entrancing narrative became for years the core of my idealistic imagination? I was always a hero-worshiper; and I think it was as a hero, rather than as a God, that Christ appealed to me. I accepted intellectually the dogma of his divinity, but I did not feel it in my heart. What I saw was the young preacher reciting the Beatitudes, or the pale, stern leader mourning over the unrepentant city, or the emaciated corpse lying limp at the foot of the cross. I was filled with a great love for this man; so much that to this day, when I should be ready to admit the historical uncertainty that enshrouds him, his figure gathers round it, in my mind, a thousand tender memories, and endless emotional reverberations. I thrill yet at the mention of his name, and hunger yet for the ideal life he wished mankind to live; if to love him and hear him gladly is to be a Christian, then, sceptic and pagan though I be, I am a Christian too, and Christ is still my God.

It was around this poetic personality that Catholicism wove itself into the substance of my mental and emotional existence. I began to say my prayers with more feeling and understanding; the lines of the *Pater Noster* and the *Ave Maria* became for me not phrases any longer, but heart-felt aspirations. Suddenly I became pious as I had never been before.

Strange to say, I did not cease to be a miscreant at school, or to give my mother trouble at home; I continued to gather in the marbles of other boys, and took eagerly to all the sports. I remember the beating my father gave me once, for stopping half an hour on the way from the store to play marbles with some chance-encountered enemy. It was well deserved, for I had been explicitly warned against delay, and the entire household awaited my return with the edibles for the evening meal. But it was the last time my father ever struck me; and he might not have struck me then had I not added insolence to disobedience. He ruled us, after our youngest years, only with a stern look and a just life; his example of silent industry and quiet kindness meant more to us than hard words or birch rods. None of us has come near him in modest strength of character and simple nobility of soul.

My father did not bother very much about the religious side of our development; he wanted us to be clean and capable lads; and for the rest he entrusted us to our mother. To her, on the contrary, our religious life was of supreme importance; she labored tirelessly to teach us the doctrines and prayers of the Church so far as she knew them. She added example to precept, prayed long, went to Mass many times a week, and gave to the Church with a wild extravagance that made my father frown a little, though he never said a word. Consequently my attack of piety impressed my mother much more than it did my father; he saw no evidence that the change within me was making me more of a man; but my mother walked with a new pride when she found that her teachings had sunk into my heart. I do not know, but I suspect that it was with her connivance, and perhaps at her suggestion, that old Père Dubois sent for me one day, and took possession of me in the name of the Church.

Père Dubois was the most majestic figure in the town. Tall, straight, white-haired, he walked through the streets in his cassock and broad-brimmed hat, and there was none, of whatever faith, who did not admire and respect him as he passed. The dignity of a great institution gave measure to his gait; and the memory of a great tragedy gave tenderness to his actions and his speech. Story had it that the old priest had not always belonged to God; that in his youth, in far-off

France, he had loved a fair maiden with all the enthusiasm of inexperience, and had been bound to her for many months in happy troth. But one day he had heard her voice crying wildly from the river; he had run down and plunged recklessly, coming to her only as she sank for the last time, out of his reach; he had himself been rescued by a friend; and then, an hour later, he had seen the body of his beloved, all bloated and blue, lying at his feet. The world had become meaningless for him, and he had fled into a seminary as a refuge from insanity and despair. Ordained, he had gone to Canada to put space as well as time between himself and that bitter scene; and from Canada he had followed his migrating parishioners into New England. Prayer and routine and somber ritual had healed him; and though he could never learn to preach well, he had a soft hand for every childish head, and a soft word for every soul. A broken heart is kind.

I did not know why he had sent for me; surely it was to scold me for my latest disobedience. And it seemed so when he spoke.

"My boy," he said, "You have given your teacher much trouble."

I bowed my head; it was true enough.

"Yes, Father," I said.

"Then why do you do it?"

I had no answer for such a simple question.

"I don't know, Father."

"I will tell you, my son. You are proud. You dis-

pleasant imagining. The gods were rather cruel to me on that occasion; I was almost dead, and had received instruction enough for one day. But perhaps, being provident gods, they were offering me an advance payment for my later sins.

CHAPTER IV

I FALL IN LOVE

ALL the evidence of my behavior in those years from eleven to thirteen drove my parents to the reluctant conclusion that I had every disqualification for the priesthood. I was a little rowdy,—dirty, disheveled and disobedient; and though I was precociously clever in my studies, my brilliance was of a conceited sort all the world apart from that willing submissiveness of mind which makes a perfect servant of the Church. I continued to be outwardly pious at the altar, and to skip less words in my prayers than the other boys; but it could not escape even the parental eye that I liked marbles better than Holy Mass, and was more interested in Jimmy Calmar than in God. In short, for a brief interval I was a normal and terrestrial boy.

And then I fell in love.

Since the escapade of the button I had almost forgotten the sexual dichotomy of mankind. I had kept away from girls, and had seen so little of them that until the age of eleven or thereabouts I presumed that both sexes had been made on the same anatomical plan, and that the essential difference between them was one of petticoats vs. pantaloons. I had sisters;

but I had been too young to observe Delia's transformation through puberty into a young lady with passions and tragedies and steady callers of her own; and Edna and Evelyn were tots in arms. Baseball and a hundred forms of sport absorbed me.

I don't know just when I became conscious of sex again. I think it was through the teasing of some older lads with whom I had gone wading in the traditionally forbidden pond that always marks the map of boyhood. I went home with a head full of speculations; and from that time I had an X-ray eye for the structural differences between boys and girls. I hunted eagerly for anything that could enlighten me; I worried my inadequate little dictionary for definitions of the mysterious technical terms which tried to conceal the truth from me; I took solitary walks, and once more, as in the forgotten past, brooded alone in my room over the sacred tabus of physiology. I gave less of my time to sport, and more to reading. I passed through the usual difficulties of adolescence.

Almost simultaneously with these troubles, and no doubt associated with them, came one of the most spiritual experiences of my life. We call it calf love; but though a calf is a pretty animal indeed, and I would not for anything offer insult to its placid grace, I protest against such a name for the loftiest and most ethereal relation that youth can know.

Near me in school sat a fair-haired, rosy-cheeked, gentle-eyed girl whom we shall reverently conceal under the name of Irene. She was a quiet lass, whose modesty was a lesson needed by my flamboyant soul. She was a well-behaved pupil, but she had a mind of her own, and could make it up when she had to. She led the girls in studies, as I led the boys; and there was a certain rivalry between us until this strange feeling of love crept into my wondering soul. Then I gloried in her successes more than in my own. I found myself admiring every move she made, and every word she spoke; I observed with stealthy and inexplicable interest her hair, her neck, her hands, and her knees (she was young enough to have visible knees). I spent many moments thinking how glorious it would be to kiss her knees.

Yes, I know quite well that it sounds ridiculous in these days when knees are no longer romantically remote. Nevertheless I record it with mad, glad candor, so grateful am I for that redeeming interlude of disembodied love. For mind you, though I was at this period all overcast with sexual imaginings, I never thought of Irene in that light at all. I longed for a thousand kisses; and beyond that only to do her every service that she would receive. I brought her pailfuls of berries that I had picked; I helped her with her lessons; I stole off, when the boys were not looking, to walk with her to her home. I was subdued and made gentle with an unprecedented happiness.

Where is Irene now? What a shame it is that I do not know, that I allowed the chaotic currents of our diverse lives to make us strangers in the world! I am told that she became a nun, and disappeared into

"I will let this go for twenty-five cents," he said, munificently.

My heart broke temporarily.

"But mister," I said, with a politeness which I seldom achieved, "I've only got fourteen cents."

He was unmoved, and turned away to another customer. I looked longingly at the book, and helplessly at space in general. Then a tall handsome gentleman, whom I conceived as a millionaire philosopher but who turned out to be a butcher, came over to me and put his arm around my shoulder.

"What do you want, sonny?" he said.

"*David Copperfield,*" I replied.

"How much do you need?"

"Eleven cents."

"Is that all? Here you are; when you get rich you can pay me back."

Fortunately he is dead now. But I was so grateful then that I could not speak. I accepted the eleven cents as a gift from God, and walked out of the store in a daze. I trudged home in ecstasy over the kindness of Providence, the goodness of human nature, and the pleasures in store for me in the 860 pages which I carried under my arm.

From that day I became a tremendous reader. When everybody else in the house was asleep I would read on, despite a thousand admonitions about the injury I was doing to my health, and the cost of gas. It is true that I lost something of my taste for sport, and more of my skill in it; I could not play ball with "Dots" Miller, or "shoot" marbles with Jimmy Calmar, any more. But what a new universe I had found! I no longer lived in prosaic New Jersey; I wandered around the world with my heroes and my poets. I discovered Byron, elocuted his address to the ocean, and went through every word of Moore's biography. I did not understand all that I read, and what I did understand shocked me agreeably. But I liked the poetry and the sentiment, and admired Byron profusely. I remember the day when I finished Moore's account of the poet's death at Missolonghi: I was overwhelmed with emotion; and kneeling, I begged God to let poor Byron at last out of the Hell to which, presumably, he had been condemned. I forgot that this was contrary to Catholic theology, and that (as the pope told the protesting cardinal who found himself pictured among the damned in Michelangelo's "Last Judgment") not even God can get a soul out of Hell once it is in. But I was horrified to think that the handsome and melancholy poet had been burning there for three quarters of a century. I felt that that was enough, even for an Englishman.

These new developments—sexual irritability, first love, and a passion for books—combined to mark my transformation, at puberty, from boyhood into youth. There was still another change, difficult for me to remember in detail, but quite as pervasive and profound, and of crucial importance in my life. It will seem absurdly out of harmony with the erotic and

Under his influence I began to take religion seriously again. The Mass became a vivid drama to me, and I saw the Crucifixion anew at every elevation of the Host. I prayed so fervently that people took it for granted that I would become a saint. I listened intently to every word of Father Morley's sermons; I thrilled under his chastisement of human imperfection; and I began myself to yearn for the privilege of preaching, the austere delight of denouncing man and praising God. How eloquent I would be when my turn came, and how I would draw all the world to Christ!

One day Father Morley came to see us in our Arlington home. He was not at his ease with women, and had little of the graceful geniality with which the Abbé Dubois had warmed the feminine hearts in his flock. But the fire of a serious mission shone in his dark face, and the women trembled with reverence as he spoke to them. My mother was all a-fluster as she sat before him, grieving silently over her unpreparedness to receive her visitor as she would have wished—with every inch of the house immaculate, herself in the neatest dress, and the children groomed as if to enter heaven.

"Your boy," he said, "is doing very well in school."

This was handsome of him, for only a week before I had been reported to him for misconduct. I stood in awe near my mother, unable to meet his eye; for this was the same man to whom, in burning shame, I confessed every week my burden of sin.

"I'm so glad to hear that, Father," said my mother humbly; "I always had great hopes for him."

"I knew you had," he said; "and that is why I came to see you to-day. Would you like to have him become a priest?"

"I'd thank God every day for it if it could be, Father. I've prayed for it these last ten years."

"And you, John," he asked, "would you like it?"

I hesitated; I vaguely realized that I was being asked, very suddenly, to make a momentous decision. I could find no other words than simply,——

"Yes, Father."

He put both hands on my shoulders, and spoke in a way which aroused in me vague memories of the similar words of Père Dubois five years before.

"Some day you will be a brilliant servant of the Church. We are going through great changes. The enemies of the Church are very powerful, and she needs new champions. Perhaps you will be one of these. Come to me Saturday morning, and I will take you to Jersey City, and enter you for the scholarship examinations at St. Paul's College. Meanwhile study hard, and remember, in your behavior everywhere, that you are called to the priesthood, and the hand of God is on you."

He went out to his horse, and disappeared down the street, trailing clouds of glory. My mother smiled on me proudly, and celebrated this second epiphany by baking an incomparable pie. As for me,

I went up to my room and sat staring out of the window for many hours, wondering what I had done with my life. This time, I felt, the decision was irrevocable. Once again I belonged to Christ.

CHAPTER V

I MEET DARWIN

I WAS graduated from parochial school that spring with a medal for "general proficiency," which (they explained to me) did not include good conduct. All summer I came to the convent near the church, and studied algebra with Sister Margarita. She had the best qualifications of a good teacher; a little knowledge, and much patience. I shrink with shame when I recall how many times I made trouble for her. Once her patience gave out, and she took me to Father Morley with tears of anger in her eyes.

"Father," she said, "I can't teach with this boy in the class. I can't control him. Either he must go or I must."

But within a few minutes he had soothed her and sent her away reconciled to my existence. Then he turned upon me with a volcanic eye that shriveled me into half of my natural self.

"Let me never hear any more complaints about you. Go!"

I went out crushed, with my tail between my legs. I was a better-behaved boy after that; and Sister Margarita came to think of me as almost her favorite pupil. Now she spent an hour with me every day, rewardless, to fit me for the examinations at St. Paul's; teaching me algebra, correcting my compositions, and going over with me the subtler mysteries of the catechism.

Late in August I went to Jersey City, and sat at a desk all day in one of the hardest tests I have ever taken. When I received notice a week later that I had been one of the three victors, I wondered whether the sly Jesuits had not passed me at Father Morley's request, on the ground that I belonged to Christ, and had to be put through.

So in September I entered college. I commuted daily from Arlington by railroad, and then walked a mile and a half through the vilest part of what I may mildly term the most unfortunate city in the United States. How strange it is that the metropolis of America did not develop there, on the west side of the Hudson, accessible by land to all the continent, and washed by the same majestic river that buffets Manhattan's shores! In place of that proud destiny the city of my first Alma Mater had become merely a railway terminus for New York, breathing the fumes of ten thousand locomotives that brought freight and passengers to the lordly Isle of Towers. Perhaps some day, when clean electric current will do the work of the world, turning its machines and moving its trains, this unhappy and discouraged city will be redeemed, and its sooty wastes and huddled hovels will flower into gardens and palaces. But I shall never quite forgive it for being what it was when I knew it, and filling my lungs with poison for the better part of seven years.

Once arrived at college, I was content enough. I found the lessons easy, and did so well that I was projected, in mid-term, into a higher grade. There the work was harder, and I had for many years to remain satisfied with something considerably less than leadership. Ultimately I became quite an expert in Latin, and achieved the useless distinction of being able to converse, fitfully, in a dead language. I studied Greek for six years, and taught it for three; and yet its classics never came to mean for me, in the original, anything but a task, a struggle with syntax and unreliable verbs; like any man, I must read them now in translation. Why should we torture our boys and girls with these once noble and now extinct forms of human speech?

The Jesuits were good teachers, and of course good disciplinarians. I have known some thirty Jesuits intimately; and all were men of superior intellect, all but two were magnificent teachers, and all but one were men of golden character. There was Father Judge, emaciated and theological, made gentle by consumption, and reconciled to an early end; never did I hear him utter an unkind word, or do any unjust deed. There was Father Ziegler, who made even Greek palatable with his bubbling good humor; and Father McLoughlin, who bore with me so patiently in the years of my mental chaos; and

Father Collins, perhaps the most capable of them all, a strong, stern man, saddened (I suspect) with an unfulfilled romance. And there was Father Gillespie, nervous and satirical, jolly and kind, who took the sails out of my conceit and helped to tame me into a socialized animal. I remember once mispronouncing "Æneas" by accenting the first syllable.

"Any ass would know that it's not 'Æ′-ne-as,'" said Father Gillespie.

"That's why I didn't know it," I answered, implying a related reason as to why he did.

He said nothing; but one day, when he entered the class-room suddenly and surprised me in some nonsense, he pulled my ear with no consideration for my dignity, and for many days I was an inverted hero. That single resort of my Jesuit teachers to direct action helped me to a better perspective of my modest place in the world.

John Moore helped me too. John was a tremendous fellow, tall, stocky and muscular, several years beyond me in age, and quite out of my reach in stature, strength and height. One noon, in the playground, a snow-ball struck me in the temple, and for a minute laid me low. When I came to, and saw the crowd around me, I could not forego the opportunity to crow; and I announced magnificently that I would thrash the thrower of that snow-ball whoever he was, and no matter how big. Moore heard me, and informed me that he was the gentleman I sought. Inwardly I groaned; outwardly I flew all my flags, and invited him to settle the matter after class. I will not go into further details; I have been humiliated often enough in this history. At four o'clock that afternoon I was in a condition of dilapidation that rivaled the aftermath of my disagreement with Jimmy Calmar. I never had to fight again at college; apparently the boys felt that I had had my share of physical education.

The reader will be relieved to know that this is the last time I shall regale him with fisticuffs. After this second slaughter I thought it wise to restrict my exploits to the realms of the intellect. I had not abandoned, even in the turmoil of college studies and college sports, my passion for the literary world; I pestered the College librarians more than any other student; and soon ran through the novels of Scott, and Thackeray, and Jane Austen, and Hugo, and Dumas. Indeed, that little collection of harmless authors was not enough for me; and by a kind of intellectual gravitation I found the Jersey City Public Library, and hauled away books at a greedy rate.

I doff my hat (or should I humble my head?) when I pass that Library to-day, or the similar institution in Newark; it was in those treasure-houses, rather than in college, that I found an education. I liked the Newark Library best, because there we were permitted to roam about among the books, and select them for ourselves. It was an admirably managed institution, offering every incentive and every aid to the student. The only tragedy was that a limit had to be placed on the number of books which one might take out at one time. As I passed among the stacks my hands reached out hungrily for this or that alluring volume; I was overwhelmed by the riches about me, and could hardly bear to leave any of the discovered masterpieces behind me when I went. I must have been a familiar figure there in those days,—at once timid and proud, bold with heresy and hesitant with thought, looking wistfully and lovingly upon those glories of literature and science and philosophy, for which I knew that my little lifetime would not suffice.

You are to picture me at this stage as a slightly round-shouldered lad of eighteen, already bending under the weary weight of this unintelligible world. I was short and almost thin, fated to be one for whom the body was merely the tolerated and neglected vehicle of a transcendental ego. I was not ugly; a prejudiced friend might have thought me presentable, had not my nose suffered a declination of its axis in some heroic football game. The lure of books had begun to pale the pristine ruddiness of my cheeks, but it had put a wild lustre into my eyes, giving me the aspect of a hunted and seeking soul. Not for many years now would I know the healing touch of peace.

One day an old Jesuit met me on the porch of the college hall, and saw from the bindings that some of the books I carried were city property. He reproved me gently.

"Don't you know, my boy, that you must not read without the guidance of a priest? Perhaps some of these books are on the Index; and you may be endangering your immortal soul in reading them."

I forget what I replied; but my curiosity continued to prove greater than my respect for my immortal soul. I was resolved to know every famous author; and when I read somewhere that Charles Darwin had written the most important book of the nineteenth century, I made up my mind that, Index or no Index, I would read that book.

In those days I was in the habit of visiting Father Morley in his new domicile as Vice-President of South Hall College. He used to wait for me on the shaded gravel walks of the campus grounds; and we promenaded together while he poured into my ears words of affectionate counsel and inspiration. I sometimes think that a priest is called "Father" because he has no children. His heart hungers like ours for the pleasures of paternity; and inevitably he finds some youth to whom he can be at least *pater in spiritualibus.*

"What are you reading?" he asked, taking up the book I was carrying under my arm.

"*The Origin of Species,*" I answered, innocently.

He frowned.

"So that's the track you're on. Do you know that this book is an attack upon your holy religion?"

"No, Father; I didn't know that."

"It is. Are you not afraid that such a book will destroy your faith?"

I answered with my usual conceit.

"It would take more than Darwin to shake *my* faith."

"Let us pray to God that it will," he said. "But your very pride is your weakness; it is in just such minds as yours that unbelief grows. You are too young to think of these things. That is why our Holy Mother Church forbids books of this kind except for those who are old enough to stand unshaken by them. It would be better for you, John, never to read another line of Darwin until you have been graduated from college."

He exacted no promises, and I went home unbound. At one moment I vowed I would follow his advice faithfully; and then I wondered what it was all about, and why this dull book should be so terrible, and what hurt could come to me from reading just a bit of it.

Nevertheless, *The Origin of Species* went back to the library half unread. Even with the stimulus of prohibition I found myself unable to grasp the argument. I had looked for proofs of man's descent from the ape; and I found, instead, an intricately detailed discussion of every animal except man. I was disappointed, and smiled with superiority at the unnecessary fear with which my masters viewed this dryasdust biologist. I decided to give *The Descent of Man* a brief trial, and if it proved no better than its predecessor I would leave Darwin virtuously alone. But I had only to read the table of contents to see that this book was to prove much more interesting, and perhaps more damaging, than the other. Very soon it dawned upon me that according to Darwin man was an animal differing only in degree from other animals, born like them, hungering like them, associating like them, loving like them, reproducing like them, and fated to die as completely and irrevocably as the lowest.

I was not easily convinced; and I made every effort to keep my footing against the undertow of doubt. I sought out the Catholic contributions to the question; I read reply after reply to Darwin; and found the refutations much easier to understand than the theory. But my pride automatically made me the antagonist of every argument I heard or read; and the more direct the argument, the sharper my hostility became. Darwin wrote quietly, without controversial animus; he had a universe of facts, and put them down dispassionately; he did not argue, and one could read him without anger. But the theologians had more logic than biology; they started from theoretical premises, and worked their ways by the most marvelous syllogisms to the most respectable and foreordained conclusions. Very often the premises were open to doubt, or the conclusions were wider than the proof. Like the theologians, I was poor in facts but had a keen nose for fallacies; I did not

two dollars a day, which averaged a quarter of a cent per comb. One Saturday, as I walked through a department store in Newark, I saw the same combs, blessed product of my hands, offered for sale at fifty cents a piece. I calculated the expense of plant, depreciation, power, shipping, book-keeping, finance, advertisement, and swivel-chairs, and concluded that I was receiving about one-tenth of my due. I understood the subtleties of "surplus value" before I had ever heard the words; and I was a Marxian before I became a socialist.

I am surprised that socialism had not come to me before. Perhaps, as one who knew factories only in his summer vacations, it took me some time to realize the difficulties of the workingman's lot; and perhaps Arlington, as a little out-of-the-way town, was slow to discover the new gospel, just as the *pagani* were the last of the Romans to hear of Christianity. Several times I had seen a young orator addressing an open-air meeting in the square near the railroad station; but as I was a better orator myself, I passed on in disdain. Occasionally I stopped and listened for a while, to have the pleasure of exposing the speaker's fallacies to my friends. Finally I chanced on an "agitator" who really caught my interest. I forget his name, I forget even his face; but I remember very well the topic of his address—"Why Must the Poor Be Always with Us?"

The speaker astonished me by discussing Christ not as a god but as an economist. He brought together certain selected quotations which seemed to make Christ a communist. He took it blithely for granted that Jesus had been put to death not for any pretensions to divinity, but for these communistic inclinations. I suspect that scholars would not bear out this view; but I was willing to accept the suggestion as within the realms of possibility. The anomaly was, said the speaker, that a man who seemed to side entirely with the people against priests and merchants and kings should have so reconciled himself to poverty as something ineradicable and everlasting.

"*Must* poverty last forever?" the young orator asked, passionately. "Are we not ashamed to let that problem go unanswered? Is there no way out?"

I did not quite agree with his solutions, but I felt the stimulation of his questions. I began to read economics, and within a week after that street-corner speech I discovered the literature of socialism. Almost overnight my interest in theology faded away. I came down suddenly from heaven to earth, and instead of asking any longer, "Is there a God?" I began to rack my brains over the question, "Is there any way out of poverty?" I fed with great appetite on the various Utopias—More's, Campanella's, Bacon's, Harrington's, Bellamy's, and the first of Mr. Wells's succession. My loss of the theological heaven left me, like my generation, hungry for an earthly paradise.

Then I grappled manfully with the three volumes of Marx's *Capital.* I finished the first volume in ten years. I became almost a reactionary through dis-

She stopped, and began to cry quietly. I bent over her and begged her to tell me just what it was that worried her. At last she found words.

"Tell me, John, you wouldn't go to——?"

Poor little mother! What a mess of worry I had given her! I put my arm around her, and told her that the thing had never entered my head. She dried her eyes and let me lead her up to her room. In the darkness near her door she caught my hand.

"You promise me, John," she whispered.

I promised.

A few months later love sang me its second song.

It was a great mistake of my parents to let me join the choir. If I remember rightly, I served as acolyte at early Mass on Sundays, and then returned to sing at the late Mass. That was well enough, and my singing was not much worse than that of the others. But it escaped the notice of my family that I was turning twenty-one, and that the organist was a pretty girl. Her name was Esther, and her hair was liquid gold. She was a wild Irish rose, coy and sprightly, and as ready for romance as I.

If we had not had so many rehearsals there might have been less mischief. The rehearsals were held in the homes now of one, now of another, member of the choir. At one of these I had an experience which produced some posthumous illumination. All the work had been done except the preparation of a duet between myself and Clare,—a woman considerably older than myself, and unwillingly intact. Her family were out for the evening, and when the rest of the choir had gone, we were left alone. For a time we practised our duet. Then, to my surprise, Clare rose, and went up stairs. Half way up she turned and beamed upon me.

"Want to come up with me, Jack?"

I had no suspicion of her meaning; obviously my mother's solicitude had exaggerated the precocity of my development. I answered with laudable simplicity:

"No; I'll stay here."

Very soon she came back, a little flushed and angry. She made no objections to my going home; I could be of no further use to her. Not till I lay in bed, safe from her charms, did I understand what she had meant. A year later a young man who had proved more responsive was compelled by law to marry her. When I saw him passing to his punishment I whispered to myself:

"There, but for my innocence, go I."

It was shortly after this that we met for rehearsal in Esther's house. I took in observantly the superiority of her home to ours, the grandeur of their piano, the depth of their upholstery, and the removability of their rugs; even their cat looked more prosperous than the lazy old Maltese who used to lie on her back on my reading board and shamelessly invite me to tickle her nipples. I noticed the business-like ability of the father, and the modest culture of the mother. I also noticed Esther.

Irene had been too immature to arouse me to passion with her physical charms. But this was a different story. Some inexplicable increase of hydraulic pressure was driving me to a blind erotic hunger. As I stood beside Esther and sang to her playing, I had all I could do to refrain from biting her rosy flesh; and perhaps I was saved from this atavism by the fact that I could not make up my mind whether her neck or her arms were the more desirable. The Reader will perceive, from this indecision, that I was already something of a philosopher.

Yet I would not let this confession of the rising tide of sex within me give the impression that my love for Esther was merely physical. When I looked into her eyes, or heard her voice, or watched her simplest actions, I fell into a trance of admiration. Even in her case the last lust never came to me; and I was fairly content to talk with her or hold her hand. But when she let another candidate hold that hand I smiled bravely to hide a heart full of jealousy and rage. I was such a fool one evening as to take to her home two of my handsomest college chums, Kevin Lynch and Tom Meaney; Kevin as clean and finely built a youth as ever Greek sculptors knew, and Tom as clever and as charming as Mephistopheles. If memory kept all details, and readers had a fund of patience like Fortunatus' purse, I could tell a Dantesque tale of hellish sufferings that evening, as we three lads vied with one another for Esther's smiles, and she divided them among us with that subtle wisdom which nature gives prenatally to women. But let me inform Kevin and Tom, wherever they are, that as I bade Esther good-night she whispered into my ear (I hope not also into theirs) these deliriously delicious words:

"Mother says I may keep steady company now if I like."

What an innocent and simple thing to say!—or am I innocent to suppose it so?—and yet what rainbows of happiness it flung around me! I hardly slept, those nights; and instead of racing through books in my room when I was home from school, I sat on the porch looking for hours into the unresponsive air. Wherever I turned I saw Esther's face, her glorious hair, her full lips, her bright blue eyes, her radiant smile, the alluring softness of her throat,—and more with which the Reader need have no concern. Already I pictured her as my wife. I wondered how, after my coming graduation, I could find work that would support us in a condition consonant with my dignity as a Bachelor of Arts. I covered many sheets with calculations of the cost of rent, furniture, chinaware, food, clothing, and the other necessary evils of married life.

What could a college graduate do anyway? There were so many things that an ordinary man could do; but the more educated one became, the fewer the fields that were open to him. I could not study medicine or law; for these required fond parents making postgraduate sacrifices, and I might rather expect exile than further aid when the truth came out. It would be a fine thing, I thought, if I could earn a living by writing; but I had already tried that and failed. Had I not written "A History of English Literature," and a novel, and some odds and ends of poetry?—and were they not lying now in the attic, tagged with rejection slips and enjoyed only by mice? What could I do?"

I wrote bravely to Arthur Brisbane, and asked whether he could give me work on the New York *Evening Journal.* He answered that there were eight hundred applications ahead of mine, but that if I really wanted a place I could have it. Nevertheless, I should be warned against the profession of journalism, for (he wrote) "reporting deforms more men than it forms." I accepted the offer and ignored the advice. I suspected that it was true; but how could I get Esther if I had no job?

What had happened, meanwhile, to my ecclesiastical vocation? It had dissolved in the light of knowledge and the heat of love. Though I kept my promise to Father Morley and prayed like a tempted Anthony I found the figure of Esther getting mixed up with the Virgin, and the economics of marriage entangled with my rosaries. I tried as long as I could to postpone the day when I should have to break the news to mother and father that I could not enter the priesthood, being drawn now towards a more normal and popular vocation. The happiness of my new love was mingled with the torture of the impending crash.

I quite forget how at last I made my mother understand that I had fallen from the pedestal upon which she had placed me. The ignoble truth was that she discovered the fact for herself before I could say a word. I remember that on returning from school one day I found her sitting quietly idle,—an unprecedented attitude for her at any time.

"Tired, ma?" I asked.

"No; only here"; and she laid her hand on her breast. "Are you going to rehearsal to-night?"

"Yes."

"Are you going to take Esther home?"

"If she would like me to."

"You are in love with her."

It was no question, but a statement, a resigned acceptance of fact; my mother had come to understand my humanity. I said nothing; and she went on.

"You don't think any more of becoming a priest and serving God. You forget all that we have sacrificed to let you go to college. Now that you have your education you don't care for the mother and father and the Holy Church that brought you up and kept you pure and sent you to college all these years when your brothers were working."

It was so nearly true that I could make no answer.

"You are young," said my mother, "and you don't know what you're doing. You love her now, but it won't last. You are not old enough to understand how hard marriage is. Oh, my dear John, you are only a boy, and you want to throw yourself away so soon."

for me; something else had gone wrong. I vowed to kill the person who had stepped between us.

That night I, age twenty-one years and seven months, cried myself to sleep. The next day was Saturday, and I was free from school. As soon as I had eaten breakfast, silently before a silent mother, I took my hat and walked up the hill to Esther's home. A great dog came growling at me. I patted his head respectfully and propitiated him into letting me go up the porch and ring the bell. Esther's mother came to the door, but did not admit me.

"Your mother," she said, angrily, "was here yesterday and asked me not to let you see Esther for a while. I think it might be a good thing too."

There was nothing more. I thanked her, and came away crushed with defeat and yet stiff with rage. I was not through with rejections. That afternoon fate sent Esther along a street where I was prowling and moaning. I almost ran to her.

"Esther," I asked, "are you willing that we should not see each other again?"

She threw her golden head back proudly.

"People think I am taking you away from the priesthood. I won't have them say that of me. Please do not speak to me any more."

This time I was quite broken; even the "abominable pride" which Father Morley had denounced crumbled in me like a shattered spine. I went away and wandered in deserted fields, calling passionately upon God to help me, and quite forgetting that I no longer believed in his existence. I might have gone to pieces had it not been for my brother Ben. I shall never forget how Ben found me walking aimlessly about, and listened to my rage and my love, and comforted me with peanuts, and took me home. What a brother he was to me that day! May I be near to comfort him, if his world should ever fall about him as mine fell about me then!

any reporter can get the news, but it takes a *Journal* man to get the picture."

I found myself, an hour later, at the house I wanted. I went to the janitress, and offered her some money for permission to get into the room which the girl had occupied. She refused; the police had evidently spoken to her a language more international than that of gold,—the language of fear. A few minutes later I made my way into the building, climbed to the roof, and as my luck would have it found a skylight over the apartment which I sought. I forget how I opened it; I remember only that I jumped down and found myself master of all that I surveyed. How a mere intellectual could have mustered up such audacity I can now hardly understand; but there I was. I went through all three rooms and gathered up every female photograph I could find. I unlatched the door from within, let myself out quietly, and escaped with my spoils.

Instead of worrying about being jailed for illegal entry, I thought only of my achievement in securing the pictures; I swelled with that pride of action which book-worms know when for a moment they have lived. Surely the editor would lift his eyebrows, praise me, and raise my salary. But when he learned how I had taken the pictures he shook his head.

"We can't use them," he said.

"Why not?" I asked, angrily.

"Because if the police found us out we'd be subject to a fine, and you'd be liable to imprisonment. We have to keep in the good graces of the police department, or else they'll shut us out from all sorts of news that we must have."

That was the sum total of my Nick Carter afternoon.

My last case was a murder in 42nd Street. A storekeeper had made advances to a sales-girl, she had rejected them, and he had shot her. When I worked my way to the inside of the crowd the dead woman still lay where she had fallen. A trickle of blood wandered from her breast along the cracks in the floor. She was a beautiful girl, with a fine profile and a great wealth of blond hair; only that morning, no doubt, she had thought of a hundred niceties of toilette, and of the lover to whom she would be true, and of the home she hoped to have. It was all gone now; a little slip in the routine of life had destroyed her, and left her helpless there, like a worm crushed by some hurrying foot in the rain.

"Have they found the murderer?" I asked a policeman.

"They're chasing him. I hear they've got him cornered in Spalding's store, down the street."

I ran out and looked for Spalding's. I made out the place at once by the crowd that besieged the doors. Within, four policemen were on guard, with drawn revolvers.

"Where is he?" I asked.

"He ran upstairs," answered one of the officers.

"Why don't we chase him?" This was an inverted

editorial "we," not intended to include the first person.

"Go ahead," was the reply. "Who's stopping you?"

I regretted the "we," and having spoken, I began to think. Evidently in interesting events there were other aspects than that of news. These policemen were thinking not of the story, but of their lives; they preferred to be outside the headlines reading them, rather than in the headlines dead. The murderer, presumably with several shots left in his revolver, was, it seemed, standing at the top of the stairs; he would make an easy target of anybody pursuing him, while he himself could remain almost unseen.

We stood there, excited and ridiculous, for half an hour. Meanwhile the prey had slipped the net; he had gone through a window and down a fire escape into an alley. The policemen detailed to guard the rear of the building arrived just in time to see him pass into Forty-third Street. They pursued him bravely, though he turned upon them and shot one dead. A driver jumped down from his truck with that public forgetfulness of danger which so often conquers the "first law of nature," and sank his great hook in the murderer's brain; but at the same moment the hunted man sent his last bullet into the driver's body, and captive and captor fell dead together. Ten minutes later the news was brought to us as we crouched anxiously beneath the stairway in Spalding's store. Three men and a girl dead; here was story enough for a reporter; and tragedy for half a dozen homes.

I was unfit for journalism partly because I had not the boldness which pierces the privacy of human hearts and ferrets out their secrets, and partly because behind every column of news I saw the suffering of men and women. Brisbane was right: these experiences were deforming me, making me hard and cynical; my idealism was passing into a "realism" just as untrue to life as my dreams had been, because the nose for news smells out the bad and ignores the good; virtue has always been less interesting than vice. Within a month of my interview with Brisbane I felt that I had enough of this work; to continue it would turn me into either a lunatic or a criminal.

It was Father Morley who rescued me. When I supposed that he had driven me out of his thoughts, when I had given him every reason for believing me irretrievably a worldling and an atheist, he still kept faith in me, and held me guiltless of my sins of doubt and love. He did not know how loathsome my work as a reporter had become to me; but almost as if he had known, he held out his hand to save me. Fool that I was for not keeping his letters!—they were all so simple and perfect in expression, and so simple and perfect in feeling; they would have given substance and fragrance to these bits of the past that I would snatch from a fading memory.

Would I come and teach in South Hall? The remuneration would be small, but the work might prove congenial, and be a stepping-stone to higher places later on. I could have laughed aloud with joy as I read; never had I had so much reason for believing in Providence, even in a Providence prejudiced in my favor. I wrote a grateful acceptance; and I hastened to tell my father and mother that though I could not be the priest they had wished to make of me, at least I was to be a teacher in a Catholic college, under the man whom, of all the priests we had met, we admired and loved the most.

I blush to relate that I was dishonest with the *Journal* after that. Instead of working conscientiously on every assignment, I occasionally imitated the trick of older reporters, who went to a show, or dozed off in the lobby of a minor hotel, and then called up and sent in, from their imaginations, a much better story than the facts themselves would have made. And like them I stole off an hour or two every day before my time. I felt that I had only a week or two left with the *Journal,* and that these delinquencies were peccadilloes. But I am ashamed now when I look back upon that fortnight; and I wish the Reader to set me down as a man capable of a sentimental idealism, but capable also of lies and greed.

I was punished by what was in effect a dismissal. One morning towards the end of August the city editor called me to his desk.

"Look here," he said, "are you sure you like this sort of work?"

"Fairly well," I answered. I was not due at South

Hall till the middle of September; I could not afford to be idle for three weeks. But I failed to deceive the editor.

"I don't think you do," he said. "You're not the man for newspaper work. You're too soft and literary. I'll keep you on for a while if you wish, as a courtesy to Mr. Brisbane; but I know you'll be more comfortable elsewhere. Suppose you take two weeks off with pay, and try to find something more congenial. Then come and tell me what luck you've had."

I thought this a very happy solution, and agreed to it with what must have seemed a suspicious readiness. It meant that I was to have several weeks' rest before taking up my tasks at South Hall. I went out into City Hall Park as happy as a child let out of school. For the first time in a long while, I spent more than a nickel on my lunch. I took an early train home, and from the upper deck of the ferry I waved a glad good-bye to rape, murder, theft, divorce, prize-fights, and Beatrice Fairfax. I walked the streets stiff with the dignity of a professor.

pothesis? How many "truths," the Church had seen come and go, how many sciences, during its life, had been born and passed away; what guarantee was there that the favorite guesses of modern thought would not seem to a later age as ridiculous as the star-reading of the astrologers, the head-reading of the phrenologists, and the gold-making of the alchemists? Science, like most history, was a fable agreed upon—for a while.

No; these matters of theory were not the important things. What counted was the tremendous effort to humanize and socialize the race; to curb the greed of the strong and comfort the sorrow of the weak; to frighten evil-doers with the fear of hell, and hold out to the unhappy or bereaved the solacing hope of paradise; to preach to all men incessantly the virtues of gentleness and kindness, and fill their dull lives with the poetry of the Sacraments and the Mass. This was the mission of the Church; and one who understood it so would put aside his frail individual judgment, and accept the teaching of the Councils as he accepted, in physical science, the reports of the savants. Individual judgment would be the end of the discipline and the co-operation which had given to mankind, in the Church, its most powerful instrument for the elevation of the race.

That (unless I am mingling later thoughts with memories of those days) was the philosophy of my friend the President. He brushed aside such difficulties as the cruelties of the Inquisition, the burning of

Bruno or the condemnation of Galileo, as the inevitable mistakes of an organization divinely founded but manned by imperfect men; he would not apologize for these bloody errors; and he would no more abandon the Church on their account than he would leave his country because it had been unjust to Mexico in 1848. Ah, a man should be loyal to his nation, should love it even if it erred; but how much more should he love and be loyal to the country of his soul, to the great faith that had built the cathedrals and painted the Sistine Chapel, the great hope that had held up countless millions of men and women in distress and misery, the great charity that had turned Europe from a wilderness of marauding beasts into an ordered home of letters and the arts!

I can imagine now what a Voltaire or a Diderot, a Lecky or a Buckle, a Schopenhauer or a Nietzsche, might have said to such an argument. At the time it had an effect upon me proportioned not to its logic but to the moral nobility of the man who uttered it, and the love I had for him. Any theory that could make it easier for me to work with him, help him, and please him, met in me the co-operation of a will-to-believe. Perhaps the material and moral filth that I had encountered in my slumming as a reporter inclined me to react away from the cynicism and scepticism of my *Journal* days. Meanwhile the almost weekly visits of my parents to South Hall, or of myself to them at Arlington, and their renewed and infinite kindness to me, affected me in the same direction. In this almost sexless atmosphere I had begun to forget the very face of Esther. I found myself wondering whether my unbelief was so vital, or my negations so certain, that I could not don the cassock and realize the hopes of those whom I loved.

At the same time a new factor entered my life, whose name was Charley McMahon. Next to Tom Meaney he was surely the brightest of the lads I had known at St. Paul's; and he was beyond all comparison the most brilliant of my friends at South Hall. He was in senior class when I joined the teaching staff; and though Father Morley looked askance on such intimacy between a student and an instructor, Charley and I used to pace the paths together for many a disputatious mile. He was a handsome boy; a little younger than I, but quite capable of following whatever lead I might open in our conversation. I was astounded, on one of our walks, to hear him mention Karl Marx.

"What?" I asked. "Have you read Marx?"

"Sure," he answered.

"Read him through?" (These questions always go together.)

"Not on your life. I left the second and third volumes for later incarnations."

"What do you think of socialism?"

He looked at me quizzically; I suspect he was a little uncertain how far he might go with a friend of Father Morley.

"I think it's interesting," he said. "What about yourself?"

I was willing to pay for confidence with confidence; it was so hard to keep all my advanced thought to myself.

"I think it's the hope of the world," I replied.

He was not so enthusiastic, but he responded favorably enough.

"I'd like to see it tried," he said. "But you know the Pope denounced it in one of his encyclicals, don't you?"

"Yes; but in the same letter he said many pretty things about the workers of the world. Most of the Catholics in this country belong to the working class, while most of the capitalists are Protestant."

"That's right; the large industrial cities usually have Catholic administrations. The Protestants get the money, and we get the people."

"Well, if our Church is the Church of the poor, why shouldn't it cast in its lot with socialism?"

He looked a little frightened, and made sure that we were not overheard.

"That's a large order, Jack," he said.

"They say that in 1889 Father McGlynn came near carrying the Catholics of New York into the camp of Henry George and single tax."

"What the deuce is single tax anyway?" Charley asked.

We lost ourselves for a while in the bogs of economic theory, and then returned to the poetry of socialism.

"There's not much chance of the Church going socialist," said McMahon.

"There is a chance," I argued. "With the right leaders, socialism would sweep the world. The Church and the workers together would be irresistible. We'd have again a united Europe—perhaps we'd have Europe and America united—under the papacy; war would stop, and there'd be such prosperity and happiness as never before in history. What a glorious thing it would be all around!"

"You're reckoning without the millionaires. They'd buy up every paper, poison the editorial and news columns and make every respectable ass in the country turn up his nose at you. You know the power of 'holy script.' The people believe anything if they see it in print."

"That's the whole point; socialism can't succeed so long as press and pulpit are both against it. But if the Church were with it, the press would be powerless. There is only one force in the world that can cope with money, and that is religion. The priest is stronger than the editor. It would be a simple thing for the priest to show that the New Testament preaches a socialist, even a communist, ideal."

"Phew! You're going fast. You're not in for equal division, are you?"

"No; of course that's impossible. All I want is that

the Church should come out definitely against exploitation, and on the side of the under dog. I want to see the Church declare a holy war against poverty and greed; I want her to make it shameful for a man to squeeze rotten wealth out of the filthy misery of factory slaves. I want her to stop idealizing poverty and meekness, and begin to stigmatize the hard-faced, ruthless money-maker, and the safely-elder war-maker, as types a thousand times worse than the drunkard, the harlot, or the atheist."

I have always enjoyed making speeches, and have always postponed to the end of my speech any consideration of the trouble I might be brewing for myself. Oratory is such an orgy that one may willingly pay a price for it. Now that I had shouted my piece, and phrased my dream, I resigned myself to having my friend turn against me, as Daly had done, for the safety of his immortal soul. But McMahon was made of sterner stuff.

"Jack," he said, enthusiastically, "I'm with you. For such a Church I'd be willing to lay down my life. I've been hesitating about entering the seminary; but if you think there's any chance of our getting some of the new blood in the priesthood warmed up to this idea, I'll go in with all my heart and soul."

"Let's think it over," I suggested, with very uncharacteristic caution. "We have half a year yet. If we feel, in June, that the thing is possible, I'll put on the cassock with you. It will be a long and patient grind; but it's the only way in which socialism can come. Once we get into battle we may find the younger clergy anxious for the move. Then, by God, we'll rebuild America, and renew the Church."

In the fall of that year we entered the seminary.

CHAPTER XI

IN THE SEMINARY

It was, for me, an act of hypocrisy, generosity, idealism and egotism. After two years of effort I had had no success in recapturing either the old piety or the old faith. I found some response in my heart when I thought of the lonely figure of Christ; but it was impossible for me to conceive a personal deity. I entered the seminary trusting that faith would come by osmosis, by the contagion of the environment. For the time being I accepted the Church as a great moral institution, and was willing to put aside my private opinions in order to work with her. I thought I was behaving like a statesman; but when I look back upon those years I see myself walking under a mountain of lies. Ah, if we could only relive our past as we would make our future; and if we could only live our future as we remake our past!

In the deceptive enchantment of retrospect the pervading motive of this new move presents itself as a desire to please my family and my friends. Strange to say, I had forgotten love; and the thought that I was foregoing the delights of marriage no more entered my head than the thought that I was also escaping its responsibilities. Here I was at South Hall, surrounded by priests and seminarians on every side; there was but a step between them and myself; and by taking that step I should with one act redeem all the injury I had done my mother, and fill her heart with an intense joy such as she might never have known had my progress toward the priesthood been undisturbed. And she loved me so much (or so I thought); she was so gentle and tender with me; never reproaching me, never even uttering a word of her hopes. But I knew that she had been praying, morning and night, for this dénouement to my devious youth. I could not disappoint her any more.

The idealism and the egotism were inextricably mixed, as they so often are. I took with Quixotic seriousness the mission I had assigned myself, of working within the Church to ally it with socialism; and I was prepared for a life of warfare to that end. But this was theoretical: what actually moved me was the vision of myself making fiery speeches for the cause, suffering contumely for it, and at last getting credit for its victory. In that dream of the future I saw my path as a Way of the Cross, with success arriving just in time to prevent a crucifixion. I would be the Pope of American Socialism, the Second Savior of the World.

So you picture me now in the flowing cassock and the square biretta, looking a little more pompous and learned than before, walking with the consciousness of my augmented importance in the history of mankind. Though I continued to teach some of the innumerable languages in which I had been instructor, I lost the privileges and emoluments of a professor. Instead of receiving a salary for my work, I found it necessary to consume nearly all of my savings to keep myself in clothing and theological texts. Instead of eating the cannibalistic meals that had been served at the teacher's table, I had to accustom myself to the ascetic diet of the seminarians' refectory. Instead of a spacious chamber and a luxurious bed, I had to share with another young saint a small bare room directly under the roof, where we suffocated in summer and shivered in winter. Many a day found the water in the wash-bowl frozen to the bottom. It required a great deal of religion to get out of bed on those icy mornings; and as I had a little less than the others, I suffered accordingly.

We rose at five, washed in a minute, dressed in two, and then hurried down to the chapel for first mass. Very often we stayed for a second mass, making an almost continuous hour on our knees. Every knee in the seminary was calloused with devotion, and almost every back was bent with the humility of prayer. Then we were free till breakfast time, which came at half-past-seven, and found us ravenous. At nine we crowded into a little room on the top floor, and Father Farrell instructed us in dogmatic theology. He had just returned from a long stay in Austria; and he combined with a Teutonic patience in study and teaching, a tendency to speak English with queer

Teutonic idioms—ending every fifth sentence with "the same." But there never was a purer heart or a kinder one.

At ten I hurried away to teach a class in Latin. My cassock made the problem of discipline easier; but my penchant for bad puns tempted the students to exercise their wit upon me occasionally. At eleven we had Father (or, as he was now called, Doctor) Morley in moral theology; this was by all odds the severest hour of the day. He was a teacher who quite came up to Nietzsche's ideal, of exacting much and praising little. He assigned huge lessons of the most abominable subtleties, and expected us to recite and discuss the lesson in Latin. We had a terrible time of it; and if any of us had not begun to hate Latin yet, we learned to hate it now. I had the advantage of having kept my Latin fresh by teaching it; and when the others failed to hold the Doctor's pace he would appeal to me as the forlorn hope of the Latin tongue. I did my best; but I remember vividly the day when I too fell down, and he turned to me like a dying Cæsar to his Brutus, with the stern words: "*Neque tu hanc rem melius studisti*"—"Neither have *you* studied this matter too well." So deeply did they burn into me that to this day I can hear him biting out those words.

At 11.45 we passed into the chapel for prayer; and at noon into the refectory for lunch. While the sinful business of eating went on in silence, a seminarian read Alzog's *History of the Church*, or some similar sedative. After that, for a happy hour, we were free to play billiards, chess, checkers, or the piano in the recreation room—most of us smoking furiously while we had the chance; or to play handball or baseball with due seminarian dignity, holding up our black skirts as we chased the ball over the field. At two we had a class in ecclesiastical history, taught by a charming young priest whose name I have forgotten (health to him nevertheless!). Then I went into the college rooms to teach—sometimes French, sometimes English. At four o'clock we were free again for an hour. At five we met on the gravel paths and recited the rosary together as we marched slowly along under the trees. This was one of the pleasantest parts of the day, for it gave us a chance to think of the things we had had no time for during the other hours. Then we entered the chapel for more prayers, and at six we had a modest supper. After a half-hour for the pipe, we retired to our rooms, and prepared our studies for the next day. At nine we filed down to the chapel again. At nine-thirty we were in bed.

I sometimes wonder whether this arduous schedule was not designed in part with a view to meeting the problems of sex. Here were forty vigorous young men, just at the age when the sex secretions break the dams and don'ts of morality: how were they to be prevented from falling in love with the chambermaids? The answer apparently had been: Tire them out. When we struck bed we were so exhausted that

Vespers, as I was swinging the censer before Father Morley, I became confused, trembled, and stopped, utterly unable to think of what the ritual called for next. For a moment the universe stood still.

"What's the matter with you, John?" whispered the astounded Doctor.

I could not answer. I handed the censer weakly to another seminarian, and took refuge in the sacristy behind the altar. I could have cursed the man who had invented so elaborate a ceremony, turning religion into a puppet-show, and priests and acolytes into actors. It never occurred to me that perhaps most people, participants as well as congregation, liked this colorful pageantry. I sat there brooding until the services were over; and then, when I expected my fellow-seminarians to laugh me down as a dunce, they comforted me with sympathetic smiles, and two or three of them took care to engross me as soon as possible in a game. The kindly President never mentioned the matter to me, and remained as gracious as ever.

I did better when it came to the annual sermons which we were allowed to preach. I selected a difficult subject, wrote a brilliant paper in which I shocked both students and faculty with my knowledge of profane literature and philosophy, and spoke my speech with the passionate eloquence of one who hungered for admiration and praise. My only reward was a gentle reprimand from Father Morley for the doubtful orthodoxy of my views.

"John," he said, "I notice that you chose a philosophical rather than a moral subject. That's a wrong lead. . . . Your congregations will not care a whit for your subtleties and your historical allusions, your hypotheses and refutations and interpretations. What they want from a sermon is a guide and stimulus to good conduct. After all, what are all the theories in the world beside a word of comfort or an act of kindness?"

The good Doctor used to honor me, in those days even more than before, by choosing me as the comrade of his walks, and even of his prayers. Though I had not reached the stage in which the candidate for the priesthood begins to read the Breviary, he instructed me in its use; and on many an evening we read the day's assignment together, verse by verse in turn. I liked the music of the Latin, and caught occasionally the majestic metaphors and the noble simplicity of the psalms and songs we read. I went to bed, on those nights, with a heart filled with happiness over his affection for me, and yet tortured with the thought that I was guilty of unpardonable deceit. Sooner or later, I felt, I must tell him everything.

All in all, my year and a half in the seminary were a tolerably unhappy time. Theology was an abomination to me. I managed to "cram" the lessons in ten or fifteen minutes before class, and to keep them in my head till the hour was over. When, in January and June, we were examined by the seminary faculty and the bishop, I reduced each text-book to my own summary, and escaped the ordeal with comparative success. My evenings, which were the only time left me for study, went not to theology, but to profane philosophy. I had been made librarian, and passed many reverent hours among the books which lay almost unused in one of the prettiest buildings on the college grounds. I came upon unsuspected treasures in the midst of those dusty tomes of dusty thought. There I first discovered Anatole France, represented only by *The Crime of Sylvestre Bonnard;* the book was so objectively written that I presumed Anatole was a good Catholic and a highly respectable Academician, who had confined his knowledge of women within the proper numerical limits. And it was there that I found Spinoza.

Why Hale White's translation of the *Ethics* should be in that pious little library the Lord only knows. But there it was; and as soon as I opened it I realized that I was reading one of the great books of the world. I was of a logical turn of mind, and liked rigid argumentation; it was at least a novelty to have a philosopher offer no blinding rhetoric, but a sternly ascetic structure of definitions, axioms, propositions, and proofs. I took the book to my room, and read every word of it, though I understood less than half. I questioned every definition, and scrutinized every demonstration; I rejected some with lordly independence of mind, and jotted down in the margin what I thought Spinoza should have said. But when I had finished the book, and then finished it again, I knew that the *Ethics* would be one of the strongest influences in my life.

The first result was a renewal of my negations. Never had the case for determinism been expressed with such scornful and apparently irrefutable logic. "Men think themselves free because they are conscious of their volitions and desires, but are ignorant of the causes by which they are led to wish and desire." Free-will was an egotistic delusion. Determinism appeared to me, in the context of Spinoza, to have a certain majesty and courage in it; man was at last strong and brave enough to face himself without lies, and see himself as part of an irrefragable web of cause and effect and inviolable law. The very thoroughness with which this view erased all possibility of miracle or effective prayer, the ruthlessness with which it reduced proud man, dressed in a little brief rationality, to the level of circles and stones, the short work it made of heaven and hell,—since it would be ridiculous to save or damn people for actions not really their own,—all this attracted me, as one must admire a blow or a word that annihilates an enemy. And this sublime interpretation of God as the sus-

Republic that he had come to believe in liberty of thought and speech as the very essence of Americanism and democracy. When he organized a series of lectures, by different leaders, on rival theories of law and government, he discovered that there was a group, as ancient as it was small, which held that government did more harm than good, and had better be abolished. These people were called anarchists. It was a terrible word, and I think even the courageous Alden must have shivered over it for a while. Most of the leading anarchists, fortunately, belonged to Europe; but there were two famous ones in America, —Emma Goldman and Alexander Berkman. It occurred to Alden that merely as a matter of fairness and thoroughness his symposium on government should include an exposition of the anarchist theory by the redoubtable Emma.

You will imagine what the white collars of East Orange said when they saw Miss Goldman's name on the expensive announcements of their forum. Every man who had cheated his customers or deceived his wife acquired a new and easy respectability by joining in the cry against the invasion of a peaceful town by this unladylike advocate of dynamite. The forces of law and Constitutional order began to work, and the owner of the hall where the lecture was to be held was persuaded to announce that he could not permit the use of his property for anarchistic propaganda. Alden, angered at this civic cowardice in the face of one woman and an easily refutable theory, announced that the lecture would be held at whatever cost.

When the scheduled evening came I left the college and walked to East Orange. The trip took longer than I had calculated, and I spent some time inquiring about the location of the hall. But I found it unnecessary to go to the lecture, for the lecture was coming to me. A crowd of about two hundred people approached; and when I saw in their van a strongly-built and masculine woman escorted by a slim, grey-haired aristocrat, I knew that the location of the hall was now a matter of no importance. I waited for the two leaders to pass me, and I had a chance to observe them carefully.

I did not like the woman. Her face was hardened by years of suffering and intellectual isolation; her manner was assertive, and her carriage as utterly without grace as her speech was without charm; I missed in her all the elements which make a woman attractive to a man. She would have told me, in her sarcastic way, that a woman may have other purposes and functions in life than to please a man; and I suppose that would be true. But I did not like the lady.

It was rather unreasonable of me, for I was at once attracted to Henry Alden, despite the fact that he had none of the physical characteristics of a masculine hero. He was not strong; he was so slight that but for the even ruddiness of his face and the energy and courage of his actions, you might have thought that he was struggling with some congenital bodily weakness. He walked with a quick and nervous step and when he spoke it was like a Frenchman—with his whole body, and with indescribable animation. Yet, with all this vivacity of speech and movement, there was something quiet about him; he moved quickly but noiselessly, and though he spoke rapidly, he never raised his voice, and never forgot the perfect manners which revealed, through the disguise of his democratic dress, the born gentleman.

Behind them walked several policemen, and behind these the crowd. I fell in, and found that we were being led to a large barn in the rear of Alden's home. He had foreseen all difficulties, and had set up a platform and several chairs in the most spacious part of the barn. It was as spick and span as any home, though the neighing and stamping of a horse could be heard from another end of the building as we entered it.

The great agitator and her host mounted the platform, followed by some intimate friends, and by the zealous blue-coats. The seats on the floor were soon taken; and behind them the rest of us stood, uncomfortable but absorbed. Then Emma Goldman spoke, and the illusion of grandeur was dispelled. We had expected a fiery denunciation of official tyranny and popular bigotry, with an exposition of what anarchism meant and how it could operate; instead we found that we were listening to a lecture on the modern drama. The speaker seemed ill at ease and certainly (as I concluded on later occasions) not at her best.

"What do you think of her?" I asked the man who stood next to me.

"She's an old hen," he answered.

"I should say," said another, "that she's more like a rooster."

Nevertheless I had to concede her courage. With her ability this woman could surely have opened many doors to respectable comfort and position. Yet she had chosen a hard lot as the exponent of a theory which, through its unnecessary association with violence, had aroused against it every established power in American life. It was laughable to see four tremendous policemen solicitously noting the words of this one woman discoursing on Ibsen, Hauptmann, and Shaw. No doubt these names sounded suspicious to the gentry of the law; surely these unheard-of foreigners were criminals and anarchists, and the officials of Ellis Island must be warned against their entry.

I walked home with an evening of experience added to my little store. It was interesting to know that there were women like Emma Goldman, and pleasant to know that there were men like Henry Alden. Gradually the life of the outside world drew me magnetically away from South Hall. The old lust of living and of literature burned in me again. I wanted to know. I longed for every stimulating contact, every educative environment, every deepening experience.

saw Protagoras reading his essay "On the Gods" in the home of Euripides; I saw Bruno preaching passionately his rebel faith to little circles in Italy, and Switzerland, and France, and England; I saw the youthful Spinoza whispering his heresies to his unsympathetic friends; and I thought that I had become one of their glorious and endless dynasty.

I had prepared myself diligently, and had read every authority that I could find,—though I remember that Frazer's many-leaved *Golden Bough* was strangely out of the list. I was at the age when sex mingles itself with every enterprise, and I had been drawn overmuch to those books which dealt with the phallic aspects of ancient faiths. Certainly I stressed that side of the subject a great deal more than I would now. My hearers liked the exaggeration, and were delighted to learn that almost every symbol in religious history, from the serpent of paradise to the steeples on the churches in nearby Fifth Avenue, had a phallic origin and significance. They asked me a hundred questions, which I answered with unhesitating assurance. They acclaimed me a great scholar, an impassioned orator, and a courageous heretic. I went home confirmed in the opinion I had long since formed, that I was a great man, and that the world would hear from me soon.

Part of the world did. I think it was on the following Friday that I was called to the telephone in the office of the principal of the Montgomery Public School, where I was serving as substitute. I had had better fortune there than in most of the schools; the regular teacher was gracious enough to send word that she would be ill all season, and I had every prospect of being allowed to continue with the class till its graduation in June. The principal had prevailed upon the Superintendent of Schools to promise me, beginning with February, the license and stipend of a regular teacher.

It was my brother Ben who was calling me from the architect's office in which he worked.

"Jack," he said, "you're in an awful mess. The Newark *Evening News* has a story, on the front page, about the Bishop excommunicating you because of your lecture last Sunday."

I dropped back from the telephone, and came near passing into another world.

"Good God!" I exclaimed, "what if that paper gets into our house?"

"It's the first edition," said Ben; "perhaps you can get the *News* to keep it out of later editions."

I asked him to meet me at five o'clock and go home with me; and then I called up the *News*. It was too late; all editions had been printed. I went back to my class and pretended that the population, capital cities, industries, and exports of the South American republics were matters of crucial interest. Not till an hour later did I see just what the *News* had said about me. The horror of impending events was mixed in me with a vague pleasure at seeing myself so prominently in print. The item, half a column long, and inescapably conspicuous, informed the public that the Bishop had learned of a lecture given by me, in which I had reduced the origin of religion to sex worship; that since I had recently taught at South Hall it was desirable that the people should know that I was no longer connected with that institution; that by my actions I had placed myself outside the pale of the Church, and Catholics should have no relations with me of any kind.

I was stunned into a sort of insensibility. When my friend Monte came upon me as I sat in a lunch-room waiting for Ben, I joked about the matter, and classified myself with Bruno, Huss, and Servetus. Then Ben appeared, and his worried face restored my perspective of the situation.

"There'll be hell to pay," he said, briefly.

We traveled home in silence. I was prepared for a violent scene; there was every reason to expect that my father would at once order me from the house. But I was greeted with comparative calm. Neither my father nor my mother had seen the *News;* but my mother had received a message from the parish priest asking her to come and see him the next morning.

That evening Ben and I went to Father Eastman, and begged him to keep the matter from my mother. Without defending either my behavior or my opinions, Ben struggled valiantly to make the priest see the matter from the human instead of the ecclesiastical point of view.

"It may kill her," he urged.

But Father Eastman did not take that seriously.

"You are an enemy of the Church," he said to me, bluntly, "and the Church must protect herself against you."

I tossed about all night trying to think of some way out. Could I keep my mother from going to the priest? Sooner or later he would get to her. Could I ask my older brothers to prevent their fellow-workers in the Arlington factory from showing the *News* to my father? But they lived in Belleville and Newark; I could hardly reach them in time; and they would have scant sympathy with me anyway. Could I go to the priest and offer him a retraction? I would have done even that if it could have saved the peace of my family; I felt that my freedom of speech was a little thing beside the happiness, and perhaps the life, of my mother.

The next day was Saturday, and I had no work. I ate breakfast with Edna and Evelyn, and found it hard to play up to their usual innocent and worry-less chatter. My mother had gone to Mass; I knew that when she came back I should have the unhappiest hour of my life. I went up to my room, and tried to read.

I did not hear my mother return; but I heard on the stairs a step which I knew to be hers. The door of my room was closed, so that I could not see her enter her room, which was at an angle adjoining mine. Then suddenly there came a dull noise, as of some one falling on the floor, and a cry that for a moment hypnotized me into a breathless immobility.

"My God! My God! Give me back my son!"

I opened the door, and saw my mother lying face downward on the floor, her grey hair disheveled, her hands clasped and stretched out before her. I went to her and touched her arm. She stared at me with wild eyes that seemed to be looking through me at something beyond, and then she cried out again:

"My God! My God! Give me back my son!"

I talked to her, but she did not seem to hear me. My sisters came in, horrified, and tried to lift her from the floor; but she shook them off; and when she looked at them she showed no sign of recognizing them as her daughters.

"What is it, mother?" they asked her. "Why are you crying?"

Instead of answering them she burst out again in her weird appeal to God. My sisters turned to me for help.

"Jack, what's the matter? What does she mean?"

I could not answer. I tried to say something, but failed. Then I muttered:

"I'm going to get pa."

I ran from the house to the factory, and had my father summoned to the gate. He seemed to know, without my telling him, what had happened at home. Several of his men, with that informative solicitude which we often show when information can work tragedy, had shown him yesterday's *News*. He could not read; but he had had them recite every painful word to him. He carried the paper in his hand now.

"So you've killed your mother," he said, bitterly.

That was all. We walked together in silence to the house. My mother seemed to be quiet now; I could hear only her occasional sobbing, and the crying of my sisters. But when my father came to her she began to call upon God with the same wild cry as before.

I went into my room, but I left my door open. A moment later my sisters entered, Edna holding the *News* in her hand.

"Jack," she said, "this is a terrible mistake, isn't it?"

I tried to tell them that it was all true; but I had no voice. Then they flung themselves wildly on their knees before me, caught hold of my hands, and begged me:

"Jack, Jack, tell us it isn't true!"

What could I answer them? They saw from my silence that I had nothing to say, and they burst into hysterical sobbing, their heads on my bed. I ran from the room half insane, and down the stairs, and out to the nearest telephone. I begged our family physician, Dr. Robison, to come at once. He answered that he could not come for two hours.

"But, Doctor," I implored, "my mother has had a stroke; she is in convulsions, and I am afraid she is losing her reason. Please, please come at once."

"All right," he said, "I'll come." He had never failed us.

I went home, and sat in the kitchen waiting for

mother and son apart because of simple faith and honest doubt! What a humorless absurdity that a difference in theology should be considered of more importance than the bonds of blood and love!

I was not bitter, nor was I lonely. Even in the heat of the event I understood what base ingratitude my apostasy must seem to parents who had stinted themselves for years that I might have an education and be a priest. After all, I had been exiled gently, without violence or hatred. It was an inevitable incident of the Great Change. Perhaps it was a common incident in every generation, as the young tried their growing minds against the dogmas and authority of the old. I thought of the fermenting days of the Renaissance, the Reformation, and the Enlightenment: in those times too there must have been apostate sons and divided homes, bewildered fathers and broken-hearted mothers. Perhaps every age had known the growth-pains of transition.

And I was not lonely, because I had already had four years of nocturnal solitude, and could not feel at once the moral isolation that was to come out of this new division. Indeed, mixed with the hot sorrow of that day there was a strange feeling of acceptance and reconciliation; in a sense it was good that the cloud had burst, and that the doors had closed behind me. Let all the doors be opened in front now, even if they should lead into lonely roads. I was an outcast, but I was free.

Towards dawn I fell asleep.

I remember little of the next day. Doubtless I spent a part of it in bed; it is remarkable how well we can sleep in the morning. It was Saturday, and I did not have to report at School. I believe it was that afternoon that Harvey Keap came to my dingy room and tried to console me with his latest poetry. For the rest I wandered about through the lower West Side, half dazed with visions and memories, trying to understand the new life into which I had been flung.

Here at last was New York. What a chaos! How could people think clearly in this uproar, or find any serenity in this degrading haste and competition? The trolley's warning bell might have had some music in it if it had sounded only now and then; but its insistent clang shrieked with impatience and irritation. The horses that still drew the city's freight over the cobbled streets were glorious animals, vibrant and firm; but the lumbering trucks which they ignominiously dragged behind them were monstrous things, that drowned the poetry of life in their shapelessness and their noise. Here and there, still in a proud minority, were automobiles, graceless in line by the side of their coming progeny, but giving to the prosaic scene a picturesque element of fleet and almost silent motion. And everywhere there were men.

It was as exciting as an esoteric and forbidden thing. It had the lure of the abnormal and unnatural. I knew that this neurotic life was not the kind of existence that would make for health of body or poise of mind; but I was attracted by the intensity of it, its variety and fulness, its adventurous complexity. The noise irritated me, almost frightened me; but I had no doubt that I would soon be hardened to it; within a week I would not hear it. This awful city had drawn me to itself, as it was drawing a million young men every year; I recognized the fatality of the process, and for my part agreed to it; here in this bedlam I would live my life, here in the heart of things, and at the foaming crest of the wave.

In the evening, hungry for companionship, I walked down to East Twelfth Street, the home of that same Freedom Association for which I had given my historic lecture on the origins of religion. The Association had been formed as a result of the execution of a famous Spanish liberal—a man whose ideal had been to establish schools that would be independent of religious domination, and less authoritarian than schools were wont to be in Spain. No doubt in America he would have been a harmless liberal. But the anarchists of New York were the only group moved to action by the cowardly association of church and state in the assassination of this great educator. As a memorial to him they proposed to organize a school in which not religious freedom only, but freedom of every kind, would be the soul of the curriculum. To teach people to be free, to let them know the happiness of a natural and spontaneous existence: what better program could there be for any school?

As I approached the little flat which had become the hot-bed of radicalism in New York, I saw an excited youth making for me with arms outstretched and face radiant with welcome. It was Dawson—red-haired, brown-eyed, bare-headed, open-hearted Dawson—one of those who through thick and thin remained loyal to their faith in a free world. He embraced me in the most passionate French style.

"What luck!" he cried. "Do you know I've been hunting all over Arlington and Newark for you?"

"What's the trouble?" I asked.

"You're wanted at the Center this evening. There's a meeting of the executive committee. Miss Bridge will certainly be glad to see you; we thought we'd never find you."

I followed him into the little office, and was introduced to Viola Bridge, Director of the Freedom Association. I stood in amazement before this strange and fascinating woman. She was so frail that her energy made me uncomfortable; at any moment it seemed that her physical resources would be exhausted, and she would fall to the floor consumed in the fire of her own spirit. Every word she spoke dripped with feeling. Her large dark eyes looked out on the world with a mixture of passionate resoluteness and brooding love; she would remake this sorry scheme of things whether it consented or rebelled. I found later that she was a poetess, whose lines trembled with the ardor of the soul that made them. It was fitting that a poetess should be the head of a group of splendid dreamers; but it was extraordinary that this sensitive plant should be the director of any association whatever. I liked her so much, after a few minutes with her, that I was prejudiced in favor of anything that she might ask.

"We are organizing the Freedom Modern School," she said, as softly as a mother speaking to her child, "to give a libertarian education to ten or fifteen children. It will be a glorious experiment; and if it succeeds, it will affect the practice of every school in America. We want you to take charge of it. We can't pay you well; and if you come to us you will be losing something in security and worldly position. But we thought you were the kind of man who would dare to make the sacrifice."

How could I escape this inveigling compliment? I wanted to say yes; it would be an exciting game, this trial of teaching without compulsion or authority; many times I had felt the absurdity and the inhumanity of the discipline which I had been forced to impose upon my pupils in the public schools. But was I ready to associate myself with the exponents of the most extreme of all movements in the world of politics and industry?

"You see," I said, "I'm not an anarchist."

"Never mind," she smiled, confidently; "you will be. And you believe in libertarian education, don't you?"

"I do." On that point I was prepared to go with the farthest.

"And you are a good teacher. That is all we ask."

I can resist one compliment; but two in a row have always overcome me.

"I should like to do it," I said. "But you ought to give me a few days to think it over. It's a decision that may affect my whole life."

"Yes," she answered; "it may. And it is hard to ask you to make your decision now. But we too must decide quickly. Mr. Black, who is the only other man whom we have in mind for the place, is leaving New York to-morrow for his school in Oregon. He will abandon that and teach ours if we ask him, but we can't delay any longer. If you refuse us, we must take him. If you are willing, we would rather have you."

I was conquered.

"I will come and do my best for you," I said.

She rose and grasped my hand as if she would embrace me.

"I knew you would," she said.

I did not learn till almost a year later what a hard fight Viola Bridge made for me that night in the meeting to which she went on leaving me. Emma Goldman, the most influential member of the executive committee, supported Mr. Black; he had had experience as a libertarian teacher, and was loyal to the anarchist philosophy. I think it was agreed that Mr. Black had everything in his favor except that his hair was gray while mine was still brown with the color of youth. Perhaps some secret and anonymous influence worked for me. At all events, I became, on the following Monday, the principal, sole teacher, and chief learner of the Freedom Modern School. In the eyes of the world I had become an anarchist.

CHAPTER II

MY FRIENDS THE ANARCHISTS

I WAS prepared to find my new acquaintances a rather wild lot. I looked for long whiskers, disheveled hair, flowing ties, unwashed necks, and unpaid debts. I had been led to believe that most of these men and woman were criminals, enemies of all social order, given to punctuating their arguments with dynamite. I was amazed to find myself, for the most part, among philosophers and saints.

I had a good chance to study the group at a lecture which I gave on "Love and Marriage." I was still young enough to suppose that one could speak an hour on this subject without providing humorous reminiscences for his maturity. Perhaps the expectation that I would make some heretical and regrettable remarks explained the large attendance. The little hall was full; and as I spoke I could see the chaotic variety of individuals which composed the actual anarchist type.

The long whiskers were there, but on one or two faces in a hundred and fifty. The disheveled hair was there, but on heads that I later found to be empty; these careless ones were neither the leaders nor the characteristic personalities of the movement. There were flowing ties a-plenty; I can still see before me the magnificent cravat of Radkon Vicoberci. As to the necks, I was too far away from them to see just how much of mother earth they carried on them. But all about me I saw fine faces. There was Stuart Dare, tall, handsome, gray-haired, quiet; a soul softened and saddened by some youthful Old-World tragedy. There was Dr. Freer, whose beard made him look more like an orthodox anarchist than any other person in the group, but whose spotless cleanliness and twinkling eyes prepossessed me at once in his favor. There was Alexander Berkman, who had, not long since, completed a fourteen-year term in prison for shooting a steel magnate in the Homestead strike of 1892. As I looked at him I felt quite secure; this man would never hurt anyone again. Not that he was too sensitive for it; he looked strong and masculine enough; but he spoke with such calm intelligence that I could not picture him reverting to the futility of violence. Years of suffering had given him a profound sympathy for the unhappy and oppressed. He joined in the discussion that followed the lecture, and with the politest indirection suggested that I was slightly mistaken in certain of my facts and views.

Near him stood his life-long friend, Miss Goldman. She listened impatiently to my prattle; she had heard these things a thousand times before. We disliked each other, I suspect, from the time we swam into each other's ken. There was something of the stern authoritarian in her which made a strident discord with her pæans to liberty; where she could not dominate she could not work. I missed in her the kindliness which I found in so many others of the little circle: they wished to help the world to peace and freedom; but she brought with her always a fiery sword of act and speech, and threatened with dire punishment a world that would not take the form of her desire. Yet she too, like Berkman, had earned by suffering the right to her opinions. From her point of view I was a young intellectual whose seminarian past made him unreliable material in the war of liberation; at any time, she felt, I would slip back into my ancient faith, and hug the old orthodoxies in which I had been bred.

Most interesting of all was the chairman, Ronald Dalton. I believe he had been born in England; certainly he had lived there in his youth; I was jealous when I heard him speak, from personal acquaintance, of William Morris, and Bernard Shaw, and Sidney Webb, and H. G. Wells, and those other brilliant apostles who had made socialism intellectually respectable for the British mind. I was jealous, too, of his tall figure, his dark brooding eyes, his handsome and sensitive face. He came of a well-to-do family, and showed in every gesture the evidences of a semi-aristocratic origin. He was an anarchist not because he wished to use violence, but because he had a horror of violence of any sort; unless he could persuade through patient reasoning he went away with his sad smile, regretful, but as friendly as before. He was incapacitated by nature from quarrelling with any man; and I doubt if ever in his life he said no to a request that fell within his physical powers. He suffered with those he saw suffer; every bit of evil that came within his experience found him, like Shelley, all nerves, and cut him to the soul. All who knew him loved him. The women in the group gazed up at him with eyes dripping with admiration and devotion; and even the men, some of them hard and cynical, looked upon him as the redeeming angel of the anarchist movement.

What did these people mean by anarchism? To the outside world, and to a certain "lunatic fringe" within the group itself, the word meant the approval of any means, moral or physical, peaceful or violent, that the exploited classes might care to use in their war for freedom. But to the finer spirits in the movement anarchism meant just the opposite of this: it was the absolute rejection of physical force as unnecessary in human affairs. This difference of opinion made the circle a nest of controversy. I can recover in fairly accurate outline one of the many disputes that made the little hall ring in those days of my radical novitiate.

"Why should we limit ourselves to peaceful means?" asked Leon Bremer, whose disheveled hair symbolized the condition of his mind. "Does the exploiter limit himself? Doesn't he hire criminals to hound out his enemies at the polls, or empty the ballot-boxes into the river when the vote goes against him? Doesn't he buy up newspapers to fill the public with lies? Doesn't he pay gunmen 'detectives' to shoot down strikers in peaceful meeting? Doesn't he organize state militias and constabularies whose secret function is to keep down the working-class? Doesn't he build armies and navies to grab whatever parts of the world he can get, by force or by fraud? And meanwhile he preaches Christianity to us: we are to be meek and humble of heart, and turn the other cheek. Well, we won't be fooled; we'll use words, or books, or guns, or dynamite, just as they come handy. Let the cowardly socialists fill the parlors with talky-talk. An anarchist is a man who dares to do things, and if necessary dares to kill."

Such language was a little startling to a beginner like myself; and loving argument almost as much as life I plunged into an animated rebuttal. I hinted to Bremer that his violence of speech covered a secret fear of action; when the time came for quick decisions and resolute enterprise he would still sit at a table in a basement, drinking tea and talking social metaphysics, as we were doing now. What he really hungered for was not freedom, but power.

"Nearly all of us love power," I announced, with that mad obstinacy which has always made me talk conservatism to radicals and radicalism to conservatives. "Freedom is an empty shell until it is filled with power. It dies almost as soon as it is born, because it is an instrument and not an end; those who get it become the exploiters of those who cry for it in their turn. The very desire behind the cry for liberty sets liberty its bounds."

There were excited interruptions, and many a head of hair shook from side to side in scandalized disagreement. It showed a fine tolerance, after all, that these passionate propagandists allowed me to go on at all. I proceeded to tell them, in my learned way, that anarchism might be possible in a simple agricultural society of the kind that Tolstoi desired, but that it would be out of the question in a highly developed industrial order; in such a society thousands of unequal functions were performed by unequal abilities demanding unequal rewards; and every increase in the complexity of industry placed the average person more thoroughly at the mercy of superior ability, cunning, or power. We were born unequal, and we became more unequal as we grew up; every new invention added strength to the strong and weakness to the weak. My discourse ended with the inopportune suggestion that anarchism was a survival of primitive isolation and simplicity, and was perhaps a secret and reactionary yearning for it; it was the beginning rather than the goal of a civilization, and became more impossible as civilization progressed. Disciplinary regulation was the alternative to industrial and political disintegration.

A handsome bearded poet stopped me.

"That is just the point," he said, with admirable

calm. "Civilization and anarchism are incompatible; let us agree. But you conclude that therefore anarchism is impossible. I conclude that therefore civilization is intolerable. We do not desire a continuance of this complex and materialistic industry which, you say, requires compulsory regulation. For my part I am willing to abandon your cities and your factories, your brothels and your slums, and go back to that primitive life in which all men were substantially equal and all were free. Yes, anarchism is an enemy to modern civilization, and to that modern culture which means the leisurely pursuit of subtleties by a few favored individuals at the cost of the slavery of nearly all mankind."

He was wildly applauded; and I could not help admire the simplicity and directness of his thought. I was ready with a crushing rejoinder, when Bremer captured the floor again, his great mop of red hair streaming out from his head like the rays of the setting sun.

"The regulation and order you talk of," he said, pointing his finger at me as if I carried the scarlet letter on my brow, "is the fetish of cowards and slaves. We don't want order, we want liberty. Order is a means, liberty is an end; for liberty is the free expression of ourselves. I don't care for production" (it was obvious); "I care for my soul; I had rather be free than possess millions. What are laws? The rules that criminals make for the quiet acceptance of slavery. Every law is an enemy of the spirit. Only when we have broken all commandments, and violated all prohibitions, shall we become men."

A pale but dark and sombre Jewess took up the argument timidly.

"If we answer murder with murder," she said, so softly that we could barely hear her, "there will be murder without end, until the most cunning and cruel brutes will be the only men left on earth. I became an anarchist because I thought it meant that all force used by one man against another is immoral. The more force a society uses on its members or its rivals, the less civilized it is. Anarchism means to me that we can get more peace without armies than with them, and more honor by trusting one another than by binding ourselves with laws. How could we do without laws or police if we were not resolved never to raise our hands in violence?"

"You can't apply the perfect law in the imperfect state," said Bremer, rising noisily from his chair.

"Then," said the girl quietly, "the perfect state will never come. We become what we do; and if we kill we'll be brutes like the rest. Only when we are brave enough to live without violence even in the midst of violence will we deserve a better life. Some one must begin."

"What's the difference between that and old-fashioned Christianity?" asked Bremer over his shoulder as he moved from the room.

"I don't know," said the girl simply.

For days the words of this little woman rang in my memory like receding bells. I was disconcerted to find so many resemblances between my old faith and this strange and disreputable philosophy. I developed a new tolerance for anarchism, and began to read its literature with sympathy. I was surprised to learn how old the theory was, and how persistently it had survived twenty centuries of political change and speculation. I was attracted above all by its educational ideal. Doubtless the adults of our own generation were too violent and insensitive a lot to get along without policemen and magistrates and jails; but why should we not take the virgin soil of childhood and sow in it the love of liberty? And then would it not be a delight to see children freed from the hundred compulsions of class-room discipline? Too long the underpaid and overworked teacher had solaced himself with the practice of absolute monarchy; democracy had shaken every citadel but that. What if the best school, like the best government, was that which governed least? To be a guide, philosopher and friend, and never a disciplinarian; to be a comrade and fellow-student rather than a teacher; to let children grow up freely without artificial pedantry or unnatural constraints: surely that would be a delight to the soul, and perhaps an illuminating test? We would try education by happiness.

So you picture me—now a slightly saddened and meditative but still vigorous boy of twenty-six—entering the portals of Freedom's school on a cold January morning. Twelve children were frolicking about with noise joyfully unconstrained. I fell in with their games, turned the play slyly into an arithmetical rivalry, and suddenly captured them with the exciting story of Columbus' voyage from Palos to America. They gathered about me hungrily; some sat on chairs, some on the table; some stood beside me, competing for the privilege of putting their arms around my neck. At this lucky juncture Viola Bridge appeared, and her poetic soul burst into sunshine as she saw how well we were getting along.

When twelve o'clock came we explored our lunch-baskets, and had a merry meal together. The children were not easily persuaded that in this world of freedom they must clean away their crumbs; but they did their best, and accepted my suggestion that those who had an abundance of food should share with those who had too little; though even a theorist like myself could see that nature had not fortified them with any instinct for such communistic generosity. Then we galloped out to the park at Fifteenth Street and Second Avenue, posed for a perambulating camera, tumbled about on the grass, and had a lesson or two in between. They never had enough of my stories of great men; when one was finished they clamored for another. "Tell us more, Jack, more," they pleaded. Astounded passers-by wondered what manner of man this was who, hatless and coatless, tumbled about with a dozen children a-top of him, and then suddenly subsided into science or history. Occasionally those who came to scoff remained to listen to these tales. Parents too would join us when they could; simple, timid mothers who had had little time for education amid the poverty and oppression of their native lands. What happy hours we had together, we big and little children, on those sunny afternoons!

There were many virtues in our libertarian theory; but there were some difficulties too. One little girl insisted on skipping rope noisily while I expounded the evolution of man; and when we suggested that she go to another room for her exercise she could not see the necessity. I thought to solve the problem by taking the class into the yard; but the pretty miscreant followed us, and jumped about more bacchantically than before. I tried the direst threats: we would none of us speak to her for a long, long time; we would let her poet-father know how inconsiderate she was; we would not let her come to our Freedom School any more. The dance went on. Finally I took her by the arm and escorted her into the street. She resisted, and protested that this was a libertarian school, where the pupils were never to be subjected to compulsion. Out she went nevertheless; and something of our educational theory went with her.

But for the most part our experiment fared reasonably well. The parents came for conferences with me, and I gave them scholarly disquisitions on the needlessness of spanking. They promised they would try to dispense with it, but begged me, meanwhile, to instil into their childrens' savage breasts some respect for a parental authority shorn of its supporting rod. The young students made good progress for a while under my easy-going rule. Some of them had known the rigors of public-school discipline, and romped through the hours inexhaustibly now, fearful that at any moment this incredible freedom would come realistically to an end. They did not call me "teacher," for that word reeked of prim authority and indigestible erudition; they called me "Jack," and looked upon me as a big brother who knew incomparable stories. When we parted at three they clung to my coat-tails till I had to shake them off and take to my heels. Many of them gave me their affection with a trustful abandon which made their parents jealous. All in all that first half-year was a bright rosary of happy days. I shall never forget them, nor those natural little anarchists, my pupils. Time and tide have borne us far apart, each from all the rest; yet in my memory very often we meet again. They are young men and women now, and would not know me if they met me on the street; but I hope there is some little place still left in their memories for their brother "Jack."

CHAPTER III

I AM BLOWN UP

It takes my breath away even now when I think of that precipitate passage, within a few months, from the quiet conservatism of a Catholic seminary to the turbulent radicalism of the most reckless organization in America. I had not accepted anarchism; but I was passionately interested in its theories and its hopes, and I admired without restraint the moral heroism of its leaders. I wondered whether these strange men and women might not also have their share in wisdom and their function in society. Our industrial development was multiplying coercions and destroying the traditional independence and individuality of the American character; our political development was littering its path with a hundred thousand laws. Democracy, incompetent and corrupt, had become a tremendous machine for the discouragement of personality, the disfranchisement of education, and the nationalization of provincial prohibitions. Never had there been greater need for a check on the insolence of elected persons, for a guard over our ancient liberties. Eternal vigilance was the price of freedom.

Therefore, when my new friends urged a battle for free speech on the peaceful streets of Tarrytown I joined them with all my heart and soul. On this matter, surely, we would all agree,—that we had every right, legal and moral, to denounce the economic and political evils of our time as publicly as we wished. How could America advance if that last weapon of minorities—unhindered criticism—was taken from them? Here in Tarrytown, we thought, was the head of a great industry; we would make his aristocratic village resound with our description of the ugly exploitation which that industry was guilty of in Colorado and a score of distant states. We would bring to his own guarded ears, to the walls and fences that shut him in from the poverty and suffering of the world, the story of what his menials were doing with the slaves he had never seen.

And so we went to Tarrytown: Berkman and Dalton and Carney and Johnson and Greb and I. Greb was a morose and silent Dutchman whose anarchism went back to the days of Johannes Most. Johnson was a Swede, tall and blond and strong as every Swede seems fated to be; he had all the qualities of his people except their geniality, which had gone from him when his younger brother, whom he loved with all the ardor of a bachelor, had been sent to jail for his part in a violent strike. Carney was a handsome and fiery Irishman; he had had much the same experience with Catholicism as myself; our common disillusionment had made us friends, and we lived together now in a lofty room on Lexington Avenue. I was French, Dalton was English, and Berkman was a Russian Jew. To an Anglo-Saxon eye we must have seemed the physical embodiment of the Black International.

We drove to the center of the town, and Carney, our finest orator, spoke for us from the rear of a touring car which a rich radical had dedicated to the "Cause." A crowd, not of workingmen but of clerks and shopkeepers, gathered about us, some curious, some hostile, most of them dully apathetic. Carney described the strike in the Colorado fields, the expulsion of the workers from their homes, their encampment in tents with their impoverished families, the battle with the company's guards, and the promiscuous slaughter of men, women, and children. Then he drew a picture of the vast estate where lived the man who, as we naïvely thought, owned the industry and the fields in which the tragedy had taken place.

"I see him at his table," said Carney, passionately; "he is surrounded with servants, and his table is heaped with luxuries. Everybody about him is silently subservient; nothing is left undone to meet his wants. He eats the assembled delicacies of a thousand fields from every continent. Suddenly, upon the white table-cloth before him a great blotch forms, deep red; and as he looks at it in fear it spreads and spreads. He puts out his hand to find out what it is; he feels something warm falling upon his fingers. He draws his hand back in fright and looks at it in terror; it is covered with blood. He stares at the ceiling and sees a large patch of it dripping red; as he looks a heavy drop falls upon the cloth. And then another and another and another. Putt! Putt! Putt! They come faster; now it is a steady drip; now it becomes a stream and a torrent of blood. He draws back from the table in horror; he tries to hide the sight with his hands, but his hands are bloody too. He turns around, but blood is dripping everywhere. 'My God!' he cries, 'what does it mean? What have I done?' But the blood continues to fall, silently, mercilessly; it forms in widening pools at his feet; it spatters his head and face; it soaks through his clothing to the skin; it covers him. It is the blood of the men and women and children shot to death by his hired murderers. Their blood is upon his head."

It was the most eloquent bit of vituperation that I have ever heard; it made me think of Robert Emmet and Patrick Henry; it was a pity that it could not go on to its natural close, if only for the honor of American oratory. But at this logical point of punctuation a piece of fruit (there were to be disputes about its species) fled through the air and struck Carney full in the face. He had not seen it coming, and his mouth was half open with the next sentence of his impassioned speech. Almost choking, he spat out as much of the fruit as had gone within, and wiped away something of the rest with hand and handkerchief. While Carney gasped for breath his friend Johnson leaped to his feet and into the fray.

"The brute who did that is a rotten coward," he cried. "Let him stand out from the crowd, and I'll go down and give him a chance to fight like a man."

No one accepted the challenge; but instead, from one corner of the group, came a volley of edibles which overwhelmed our second leader. Most of us were harmlessly bespattered; but Johnson's lip was cut with the pit of a peach, and blood streamed down his chin. The younger ones among us burned to jump out and fight; but Dalton urged us to be patient.

"If anyone is seriously hurt here," he said, "we shall be blamed, and not those who provoke us. Perhaps there are Americans enough in this crowd to give us a hearing."

But at that moment a voice contradicted him.

"Down with the dirty anarchists!" it cried.

"Ride them out of the town," suggested another.

"Tar and feather them."

"Hang them."

Johnson leaned out from the car and spoke again, biting out each word with bitter emphasis.

"Very well. You don't believe in the right of free speech. You refuse to let us make our protest against industrial feudalism and tyranny. But there are other ways than words to make ourselves heard. You've had your choice."

At that moment a patrol-wagon clanged and clattered alongside us, and disgorged a squad of policemen. They were led by an enormous officer, puffing with patriotic authority, and longitudinally ornamented with brass buttons that looked like supernumerary glands. He mounted our car and took Johnson roughly by the arm.

"You're under arrest," he said. And then, surveying us magnificently:

"You're all under arrest," he announced.

I had been excommunicated, but never arrested; this was a novel experience for me. We were escorted unceremoniously into the patrol-wagon, and our ride to the station began to the accompaniment of jeers from the crowd. Those who sympathized with us maintained a dignified silence. As we rode along Carney cleaned his face and clothing, Johnson wiped the blood from his lip, and I prepared a speech for the court.

But the sergeant whom we faced at the police-station had no literary taste, and would listen to no speeches. He scowled at us over his spectacles, asked us questions with the rigidity and invariability of a mechanism, took the bail which our rich friend sent up for us, and ordered us to appear for trial the following Monday morning. We marched back to our car without enthusiasm, and drove towards New York debating methods of revenge.

That Saturday evening I stayed late at the Center, and did not reach home till midnight. Carney was already in bed; and thinking he was asleep I undressed without turning on the light. But when I was lying still beside him, in the darkness of our little room, he startled me by saying, quietly:

"Jack, I want to tell you something."

I was all attention.

"What is it, Will?"

He hesitated strangely.

"Do you believe in anarchism?"

"Yes and no. But I thought you were going to tell me something."

He was silent. Then——

"I won't see you after to-morrow. I'm leaving town."

This had the air of a prelude.

"What's up, Will?" I asked. "Trust me; I'll stick by you to the end."

He laid an arm across my body affectionately.

"Jack, I'll trust you. We're going to blow up John D.'s palace to-morrow."

My heart stopped. I had heard so much talk of violence that I had never taken it seriously; I had supposed it was a theory, and would never come to deeds.

"Good God!" I whispered, "who put you up to this? I know: it was Johnson. Tell me."

"Johnson, Greb and I have sworn to do it. We don't want to kill anybody; but if we do, it's their fault. If we can't tell the old man what we think of him we'll put him where he won't care."

He laughed the pleasureless laugh of an embittered man.

"Which is better," he asked,—"to be a live pauper or a dead millionaire? Perhaps I shall soon be a dead pauper."

He had been out of work for some time, and had long since reached his last dollar.

"You're going too fast," I said. "You don't really want to do this. You'll be caught, and they'll give you a life-time in jail."

"Well, I'll have regular meals," he answered.

"But this man you're going to kill may know less about the Colorado affair than we do. He's an old man; he doesn't play any active part in the industry any more. It is possible he had nothing to do with our affair in Tarrytown. Perhaps he was a thousand miles away."

Carney could not realize the actual truth of this conjecture. He sat up and looked at me angrily. A ray from the moon came through our solitary window and set off his silhouette against the dim light. His red hair disheveled, his body naked to the waist, he might have represented either a devil or a ghost.

"Look here, Jack," he said, "you never did believe in anarchism, did you?"

"If you mean trying to live without bossing people, I'll go as far as you like with you. If you mean killing people, I think it's insanity."

"Don't they kill us?" he growled. "Do you want us to stand for all their damned murder and robbery without lifting a hand?"

"We have to educate them," I said, lamely. "It's

slow work, but it gets results sooner than killing."

"You're rotten with books," he replied. "You think too much. We're tired of thinking and talking and reading and educating. One bomb will educate faster than a hundred schools."

For a while we were silent. He lay down again, and turned his back to me.

"Suppose you kill them all," I argued, "all the exploiters. Don't you know that new exploiters would come up out of the exploited? Isn't that what has happened everywhere in the clothing industry? What's the use of merely changing masters, unless we can change the minds of people so that they won't care to exploit when they get a chance?"

"Rot," he said, wearily. "Even if you were right, I'd go on with this job just the same. I'll have revenge."

I talked on, accumulating arguments; but when I paused for a reply I discovered from his regular breathing that he had fallen asleep. I lay awake beside him all the night through, facing the problems of social strife as I had never realized them before, and wondering how I could save the life of an enemy whom I had never seen, without endangering the freedom of my friends.

At eight o'clock the next morning some one knocked softly at the door. Carney must have been half conscious, for he jumped up at once and admitted Johnson and Greb. Johnson carried a black suit-case, whose very color seemed ominous to me. He laid it on the floor side downwards, and then looked at me dubiously as from the bed I gave him greeting.

"Is Lemaire coming with us?" he asked of Carney.

"No. He thinks we're crazy."

Johnson scowled.

"Did you tell him?" he asked.

"Yes," said Carney.

"You're a fool," said Johnson.

Carney sat on the bed, quite naked, and brushed his hair sleepily from his eyes.

"Maybe I am," he muttered. "Maybe we all are."

"What do you mean?" Johnson demanded.

Carney made no answer, and did not move. Greb took out his watch, and remarked on the need of haste if they were to make the train to Tarrytown. I still lay in bed, wondering what to do.

"Johnson," I pleaded, "don't go."

He looked at me scornfully.

"Pussyfooter," he said. "You stay where you are, and keep your mouth tight. If the police hear of this we'll know who told them; and we'll get you if it takes a life-time. Remember."

"I'll remember. And you haven't anything to fear so far as that goes. But for your own sake, for the sake of the whole movement to which we belong, don't do this. You'll put things back half a generation."

He ignored me, and turned to Carney.

"Are you quitting too?" he asked, towering over him.

Carney looked up at him wearily.

"Sit down, Johnson," he said; "let's think a little."

"Think?" Johnson cried,—"what for? The time for thinking is past. I'm through with thinking."

"Yes," said Carney. "But I'm beginning."

"So you're afraid."

"I don't know. I'm not afraid of death, I'm afraid to kill."

"You lie. You're just trying to cover up your cowardice. Why didn't you quit at the beginning? It's too late now; you'll have to go through with it."

He went over to the suit-case, unlocked and opened it, and took out a bundle of rags which he laid upon our little table. From the rags he drew a black box half a foot square. I could see no fuse, but I knew it was a bomb, and I breathed faster. Johnson held the bomb in his hands and laughed the same dry laugh which had struck me in Carney the night before.

"Here," he said, "is the present we have for the old man in Tarrytown. Ladies and gentlemen, let me introduce you to his majesty, Death. With this little black box you solve all your problems. You never have to pay the landlord again, you never have to drag your weary body to the shop again, you find a way of making your wife love you once more. With this you escape the next war, and the hell they call peace. Who will have it?"

Greb lost something of his taciturnity.

"For God's sake, put that down," he begged.

Carney was not afraid.

"Let's see it," he said, quietly.

protest; my heart went out to these simple souls who fled from poverty and injustice into ideal and perfect realms, and covered with passionate poetry the harsh realities of life. I came now to feel toward anarchism very much as I felt toward Catholicism: I could give it respect and sympathy even though I withheld belief. But I bore from that moment a new sadness in my heart as I realized that I was fated, bit by bit and day by day, to lose my Utopian aspirations as I had lost, in younger days, my hope of immortality and heaven. This double bereavement—of faith in a redeeming happiness beyond the grave, and then of belief in a paradise for our posterity on the earth—was to be part of my inevitable destiny, as it was part of the destiny of my generation. We were caught in the chaos of transition, and would have to live through it as best we could, until a new order and a new stability of soul would come to give our children's children peace.

CHAPTER IV

I ESCAPE MARRIAGE

I HAD been but a week out of the hospital when a letter came which lifted me to happiness. It was from Henry Alden, and was postmarked "Vienna." Alden was a great traveller, and almost every summer saw him wandering in Europe or Asia. I have lost his letter; but I remember the heart of it well. "I am glad to hear," he wrote, "that you are making good progress at the school. There is only one thing you need now to complete your education; and that is travel. Would you care to join me in a tour of Europe? Of course I will pay all the expenses."

Would I care? I filled with laughter the quiet room to which I had retired after my adventure with dynamite, and rang half a dozen telephones to announce my good fortune to the world. I wrote to Alden telling him that this was a boon I had done nothing to deserve, and that it was ungrateful of me to doubt Providence now. Had I not dreamed for years of the day when, after long stinting and saving, I might sail off to see England and France and Spain and Italy and Germany, and perhaps even Greece; dreamed how I might at last murmur a prayer in the Acropolis like Renan, and worship in the Sistine Chapel like the pagan Goethe, and bask like Nietzsche in the sunshine of St. Mark's? I could scarcely believe that I was about to see those sacred monuments of man's creative passion; not till I stood in the flesh before them would I know that this vision was something more than the mirage of my youthful fantasy.

The days passed anxiously for me after that letter was despatched. I calculated again and again the time it would take to reach Alden, how far it had gone now, and whether he would reply by letter or by cable. Meanwhile, nervously resolute, I carried on my work at the School until my summer vacation began. Eleven days went by, each more feverish than the day before. Then a messenger stood at my door with a cablegram:

"Meet me at the Hotel Europe, St. Petersburg, July 10–12.—Alden."

"Good God!" I cried; "Alden writes as if he were asking me to meet him around the corner. St. Petersburg—it's half way across the world. Can I make it by July 12th?"

Within half an hour I was at a steamship agent's office. The *Mauretania* was sailing on July 1; there was still time to make reservations and get a passport. I rushed back to my room; and though I had five days left me before sailing, I began to pack at once.

On the eve of my departure I went to Arlington. I had not seen my parents for half a year; and they had uttered no word of reconciliation. Brother Ben had kept me informed: my mother, after three weeks of illness, had resumed her routine of household cares, and never mentioned me. Yet I could not go to Europe without bidding her good-bye. I exaggerated the risks of an ocean voyage, not knowing that the dangers were chiefly internal; I thought, dramatically, that this might be the last farewell of all. But would my mother receive me? I held my breath as I rang the bell at the door of my old familiar home.

There was no answer. I rang again, and again there was no answer. I felt myself caught in an anticlimax: I had prepared the most touching speeches, and could not bear the thought that they might never be uttered. I walked alongside the house to the rear, and there, at the farther end of the yard, I saw my mother working among the flowers. She turned white as she recognized me.

"John," she said, almost inaudibly.

She came over to me silently, and embraced me. I had feared that my visit would give her new hopes of my return to the faith, and new pangs of hope deceived; but she saw at once that I had not come for that; and her face quieted into a melancholy resignation.

"I'm going to Europe," I said. "I'll be back in three months. I just wanted to say good-bye."

"Europe?"

She could hardly understand. I explained Alden's generosity; and I could see it pleased her to learn that any one should think enough of her wayward son to extend him such bounty.

"It's dangerous to cross the ocean," she said. "I'll pray God to take care of you and bring you back safe. And you, John, pray God to bring you back to your holy religion."

Poor mother! What did it matter which religion we professed, or which philosophy we believed, any more than which language we spoke or what clothes we wore? The chromosomes had more to do with us than these external and accidental things. What really mattered was that you were the tenderest of mothers, and that I, having none of your faith, could love you and honor you more than this pen can ever say.

A week afterward I was in mid-Atlantic. No later experience on my trip meant as much to me as those five days of uninterrupted sea. I tired at last of looking at it, but not till I had studied a score of its endless forms: the chaste light of the chill morn turning the dark deep into white-capped vales of green; the blazing glory of the noon-day burning a pathway from the horizon to the ship; the changing rainbows of the setting sun reflecting their kaleidoscope in the sea; the new moon silvering the waters with her rays; the waves mounting gigantically to smash in fury against our iron sides, then calming themselves into the smooth billows of some inland lake; and most fascinating of all, the wake of our great vessel, the churned white froth that danced and laughed behind us, in a narrowing path, mile after mile, till we lost its ending in the sky. No wonder the proud poet had bowed in awe before this turbulent immensity, whose helpless passion outdid his own; surely there was nothing in the world so impressive as this infinite and sombre sea.

Tossed up and down in the hollow of the ocean, our giant liner seemed but a bit of unguided wreckage, and we humans who blackened its decks were microscopic animalcules creeping blindly on a floating spar. Sometimes when the prow of our vessel sank down into some abyss between the waves I thought we should never rise again; and when the hills of foaming water gathered and hurled themselves upon us I wondered would they not topple us over into a choking death. One night there was no moon, nor any star; then our great ship, ghastly alight in the engulfing dark, seemed like a phosphorescent insect struggling in the sea. But as we neared the rocks of Britain's ancient shore the mood of my thinking changed, and I marveled not at the vastness of the ocean but at the courage of man, who had ribbed it everywhere with the paths of his floating cities; who had dared to make great arks of heavy iron and fill them with thousands of tons of the products of human hands; who had built upon these frames luxurious homes for many hundred men; who had made engines capable, through the expansion of a little steam, of propelling this enormity of steel and flesh safely and quickly across the widest seas, making the

Of course I had no right to see Russia so darkly. I had come as an ordinary tourist, and had seen only the exterior of the land. I had had no access to great scientists like Pavlow or Bechterev, nor to great composers like Rimsky-Korsakov or Stravinsky, nor to great writers like Gorki, Andreëv, or Artzibashev. I know now that out of that backward country, whose inhabitants seemed never to have had a bath, there had come the finest literature of the last half-century; that in fiction and prose drama these barbarians had given to the world the greatest work ever done in those literary forms. I did not have eyes enough to see, behind the apathy of 1912, the furious energy and miraculous devotion of 1917.

At Sebastopol Alden engaged a three-horse *drozhky*, and with this lively *troika* we galloped from one end of the Crimea to the other, past the palaces of the Czar and the playground of Tolstoi to the Newport of the Russians, Ialta. I became accustomed to butterless meals, and *tschav*, and *borscht*, and *pirozhkin*, and the ubiquitous samovar. I learned that every diet is a prejudice, and that the small intestine will make humanity out of anything reasonably resembling food.

At the same time Alden learned the arts of bribery. We steamed back to Odessa, and wished to take the first boat thence to Constantinople. That vessel, however, was leaving the next morning, and Russian law required that the police should have our passports three days before we could be permitted to depart from the country. It cost Alden a pretty sum to abrogate that law; but then, no doubt, the law had been made for such occasions, and such purposes.

I did not see much of the unfortunate people who have to call themselves Constantinopolitans. All that I remember of them is the patience of their shoulders (which served them as horses and trucks), and the indecent spaciousness of their pants. I hardly dared look at those fierce Turks, and I wondered whether they had stopped beating their wives yet. You see that I was an unimaginatively provincial person, incapable of leaving my environment at home, and secretly wishing that all the world were like the familiar faces and places of my youth. I growled at the people of Smyrna, and wished they would make more use of the water which nature had so lavishly offered them; and I vowed I would never eat figs again if they came from this filthy port. But in Athens everything pleased me except the heat.

Even Pericles would have been glad to have so fair a capital,—the cleanest and most orderly city I had seen since passing the customs' gauntlet at Wirballen. I went in swimming at the Piraeus, because I had heard that Socrates had bathed there some years before,—though this item of information was quite out of keeping with all else that I had learned of the habits of that famous idler. But there were more rocks than gad-flies in that sea, and I came away with a bad cut which I still display as an evidence of my philosophic lineage. I had my picture taken in the prison of Socrates (so our guide called it, but the villain had no reputation for archeological veracity); and I reflected how sweet it would be to take the gentle anesthesia of hemlock as a martyr to metaphysics, at the age of seventy-one. And then I stood in the Theatre of Dionysus, marveled at the vast mountain-side of stone and marble seats rising in a semicircle before me, and imagined that I saw Antigone leading blind Œdipus to Colonus, and Hector bidding farewell to Astyanax and Andromache. For a moment that ancient and youthful civilization came back to me with the reality of things seen rather than of things read: I saw Æschylus writing his warlike epitaph, forgetful of his tragedies; and Pericles sitting at the feet of the learned and yet lovely Aspasia; and Socrates inviting his executioners to support him at the public expense; and Aristotle teaching Alexander to die of drink at the age of thirty-three. They had no sanitary plumbing then, and no electric lights, and no motor-cars; but they had *parrhasia*—that brave liberty of mind and speech which is more precious to the world than all its engines and all its laws.

At Athens Alden and Dan, having seen Western Europe many times before, deserted me, and alone I took the train for Patras. Riding through a paradise of vineyards I munched for half an hour luscious and seedless grapes larger and sweeter than any that had ever entered me before. And then the boat to Brindisi, and lo, I was in the fairest land of all.

Others have raved about Italy, and does it follow that I should not? But long since I have upheld it as the greatest of all the nations of Europe. Greece had her incomparable epoch; but it passed like the flush of love. Italy never quite reached the exhilarating heights of the Periclean age; and yet for two thousand years she showered genius upon the world. From Numa and his laws, and Ennius and his verses, and Cæsar and Cicero, and Lucretius and Virgil, and Horace and Ovid, and Trajan and Hadrian, and Antoninus and Aurelius, and Julian and Justinian, and Leo and Gregory, and Dante and Petrarch, and Giotto and Donatello, and Leonardo and Raphael, and Michelangelo and Cellini, and Correggio and Titian, and Machiavelli and Bruno, and Tasso and Ariosto, and Galileo and Palestrina, down to the weary wisdom of Leopardi's verse and the weary music of d'Annunzio's prose,—tell me, all ye Muses of history, was there ever elsewhere such a dynasty? Has any other nation held in its loins the seminal virtue and fruitfulness of this passionate and inexhaustible people? Look into their eyes, and you see the burning sun mirrored in twin lakes; look at their carriage and you see royal Cæsar; feel the hot lava of their volcanic speech and you know the ambitions of the Borgias and the passions of the *Inferno*. Alfieri was right: the man-plant grows stronger in Italy than anywhere else on this planet Earth. Oh, when shall we see Italy again?

I passed over the Apennines and through Sorrento, and put up for a time at Naples. I liked the people more than their cities; I hated the dirt and stench of Naples, but I envied these handsome and terrible men their beautiful and terrible women. One of these—not the least beautiful, and not the least terrible—allured me with her great black eyes and her voluptuously rounded figure as she passed me on the street at night; I followed her for half a mile as if a chain had bound me to her, until at last she disappeared into a pretentious dwelling. I remained for a long time outside, wistfully looking up at the closed door, fretfully wondering why I might not enter and tell her how beautiful she was, and consumed as I had never been before with the hunger of flesh and blood.

When I trace in memory the incidents of those happy days I mourn to think how much escaped me, and how little I carried away with me from Italy. I passed through the ruins of Rome, sad embers of a flame that burns now on other hills (or is it destined to light those hills again?), and through the streets and galleries of Florence, where beauty is lavished upon one as it might be in paradise; and always my insane ambition was to see as much as possible in the shortest time. I left myself no leisure to study these immortal things; I came to them without background or context beyond a name and a date or two; I was all eyes and no brains; and too late I found that eyes without brains cannot see. I forgot the sights of yesterday as soon as I saw today's. Though I was twenty-six I was not yet prepared for travel; I was too immature to know what beauties to seek, and too uninformed to understand those that I found. Life will be merciful to me, perhaps, and will let me see again that bright fairyland of genius. Then I shall look at less, and see a little more.

For Venice I needed less instruction; St. Mark's would open any eyes, and the music of those omnipresent waters would stir responsive harmonies in any breast. How picturesque the gondolas were; and how I liked to sit in them for hours, and talk in my pitiful Italian with those philosophic gondoliers! On every side majestic edifices challenging mortality, graceful bridges throwing friendly arms over meandering canals, sombre cathedrals whose beauty bore the memory of a thousand patient hands, and whose cool naves, large enough to hold a city, felt only the step of aged women and irreverent travelers. In the Piazza San Marco, where Nietzsche loved to sit and write, till the sunlight hurt his eyes, I wondered how the great iconoclast could have been so bitter against Christianity, here where it had uplifted men with its legends and inspired them to dream of loveliness. From my little room I could see the flowing life of the city's peopled streams, and yet hear no noise but the ripple of the gliding boats and the voices carried on the water. Byron did well to come here with his Guiccioli, and a thousand geniuses with their Muses and their mistresses. Shall not we too, some sunny day, in the peace of that floating marble, renew our youthful love and write masterpieces for eternity?

I saw Vienna hurriedly, and Frankfort and Mayence; and there I took a steamer down the Rhine. From Cologne I went by train to Brussels, and thence, after a day, to Antwerp. They were all beautiful cities, mellow with recollections, and ruled with such a minimum of incompetence and corruption as would be considered indecently abnormal in America. And then I boarded the boat for England.

I had not known seasickness yet. Now it came to me with such force that the experience should suffice me forever. I believe our little ship pointed her nose at every invisible star on that unlucky night, and distorted herself into every figure known to geometry. It was impossible to stand, or to sit, or to lie in bed; even the sailors moved cautiously along the railings, and stopped at every turn to pay their tribute to the sea. Rolled ruthlessly out of their berths, precipitated ignominiously from their chairs, and cheated at every turn of the solacing liquors with which they would have drowned the memory of Neptune's insolence, the passengers decided that the one safe position was to lie upon the floor, from which there could be no further fall.

I lay prostrate with the rest, indifferent to human affairs. Perhaps it was at that time that I lost so much of what I had absorbed upon my tour. My very vitals seemed to have cut their moorings, and resolved to explore the external world. The thought came to me that our tiny steamer could never weather such a storm; that the next lurch would flood us, and the next one empty us out into the hungry sea. I waited impartially for the event. I had no desire for further existence or experience; the supposedly everlasting instinct of self-preservation was asleep or dead. Nothing in the dark beyond could be any worse than these repeated convulsions that tore the flesh from one's throat, and spewed one's blood upon the floor. The grave would have been a victory now that death had lost its sting.

The little drama continued all the night. As we neared Hull in the morning the water calmed, and those of us who cared to stand found it a possible position. An hour later we sat shivering in an early train for London, drenched and almost blinded with fog, sick and pale and emaciated as if we had passed through a Thirty Years' War. I can always reduce the misfortunes of life to a modest perspective by remembering the tortures of that endless night. The English Channel should be abolished as an enemy of the human race.

How could I love England after that? What traveler could forgive the embarrassment of such an introduction? And yet, as I left my hotel the next

always trust the tongue to conceal the heart. It would be so much more satisfactory to believe that Ariel fell in love with me at first sight! As for me, I do not know if we should call that first-awakened curiosity by the full-bodied name of love; but from the first moment there was something in Ariel that captured my eyes and possessed my memory. I was attracted by her high spirits; she romped and babbled and laughed and sang with the innocence of a girl who had never known theology. In the park she jumped the highest, and ran the fastest, and tired the last or not at all. Vividly I remember still how we would stand alert in our handicap positions on the gravel-paths of Central Park, I on the starting-line and Ariel only a bit ahead of me, and a gay-colored rosary of children strung along the line; and how that wild fairy of a girl would leap like a spirit over the earth and race to victory. That is why we called her Ariel: she was as strong and brave as a boy, and as swift and mischievous as an elf.

In class she found it difficult to be quiet; she was not made for the artifice of study, and her vibrant body was like a string stretched taut and waiting for release. Yet she took the lessons patiently, listened in wide-eyed rapture to the stories I told, and helped me to keep the younger ones in leash. After class she was the last to go. Many times I looked through the window to see her darting across the street to her home, her brown arms swinging, her perfect body singing aloud with health. I called her my "Whitman girl," for surely she personified the *Song of the Body Electric*, and the spirit of the open road, as no other girl that I have ever known.

When Ariel danced into my orbit she was such a contrast to me as might have augured immediate incompatibility. I was all learning, and she was all life; I knew ten thousand books, and she knew only what nature and hardship had taught her,—though these lessons were sounder, perhaps, than any that had been dreamed of in my philosophy. When I heard her story I marveled at the resilience of the human body and soul. She had been born in a Russian ghetto fourteen years before; and many the story she could tell of Mershe Lebe and the other scholars in her family. Her mother had been the belle of that Proskurov village;—I could believe it, seeing her beauty now, and that inexhaustible health and energy which made her the sister of her children. What tragedies they had had! What wars, and famines, and pogroms! What bloody memories of Cossack and Pole invading homes to steal and rape and slay! I could hardly credit those tales,—men would not act so—until I learned how they behaved in the wars and revolutions of our own day. No wonder there was bitterness in the souls of those who had survived these terrors, a lingering fear of neighbors from whose apparently civilized ranks murderers might at any moment step out to tear their children limb from limb before the mothers' eyes.

"We had heard of America," said Ariel, "as a

refuge for the oppressed and the home of liberty. So father and mother resolved to come here. They might never have left home if they had foreseen the suffering they would go through on the way. Father came first, and worked and saved; then mother came with six of us—Morris, Sarah, Harry, Flora, Mary, and me. In London Mary nearly died, and Morris had to play the part of father, running about for doctors and medicines and food. Mother spent then nearly all the money she had saved. We were sick every day of the trip across; they gave us filthy food, and wherever we went the odors of the kitchen suffocated us. When we reached Ellis Island we were all thin, and penniless."

Yes, it was the story of thousands and thousands of eager souls who had bravely cut their old-world roots and taken the adventure of America. Many of them, I knew, had still to find their footing here, and were unhappy; some of them were to be sent back in that wave of cowardice which came upon us after the war; but the great healthy majority of them had risen with miraculous courage out of this prelude of despair; everywhere in America now they were tilling fertile fields, building homes, and sending their merry children to school. And here was Ariel, after all those sufferings, as healthy as mountain air, as happy as love returned, and as bright as the sunlit sea.

One evening I sat alone, in the dark, at the same table at which, that afternoon, I had told the children the story of Spinoza. (I had an absurd passion for telling them the lives of the philosophers.) In an hour or so I was to lecture on "free love." It was unwise of me to take such a theme, and to flay the unfaithfulness and insincerity which hid under that fair phrase, before an audience of men and women who for the most part believed that legal marriage was slavery, and lived in unions sanctioned only by mutual consent. But in those days I cared as little for convention and tradition as any youth; and it was not for respectability's sake that I protested against these fly-like matings on the wing. I was hungry for love, and would have preferred to have it free of all bonds and costs. What I saw as I looked about me, however, was that the men were profiting, and the women losing, by this pleasantly primitive marriage. I was resolved to ride forth, like another Galahad, and defend the still dependent sex against this subterfuge of the irresponsible male.

Then into the dark circle of my brooding came a quick step, a dim figure, and Ariel sat across the table and smiled into my face. As I looked into her eyes I felt myself in the presence of life itself. Here was the primal mystery—that subtle and yet inexplicable power of expansion and growth which had spread in a million forms over the earth. These brown eyes danced and burned as if behind them all the forces of creation surged; this softly-rounded face quivered with sensitivity, this tense body, even when still, trembled with action and desire. Now I knew that the body and the soul were one. Instinctively I understood that I had come upon a force as strong and persistent as my own, and that it was enveloping and absorbing me. Ariel could not know how the race was speaking through her, through her slender little hands, the smooth skin of her cheeks, the fragrance of her hair, the rich color of her lips, and the alluring lines that drew my furtive eyes from her soft throat to her breast.

"Miriam sent me," she said gently, "to ask if I may listen to your lecture to-night."

I knew the lure of prohibitions, and how useless they would be now. Here, I told myself, was the first girl I would save.

"Yes, Ariel; though I'm afraid you won't understand."

"I may understand a little," she said, humbly. "I so want to learn, and grow up, and be a woman."

Poor Ariel! What queer fever of growth was it that made this happy girl long to pass from her carefree youth to the sufferings of womanhood? What powerful tide of development was pushing her on to the brink of death that she might snatch a little life from nothingness?

Now she stood beside me, trembling, and looking timidly into my eyes.

"Do you believe in free love?" she asked. Then, seeing my surprise, she drew away, and stood across the table from me, sorry that she had been so frank.

"I'm going to talk about it in my lecture," I said.

"Some time you'll tell me what you think of what I shall say. But don't think too much about it; you've plenty of time. Why should you want to grow up so soon?"

She looked at me trustfully, and smiled. I rose hastily, and retreated from the field of battle to the safer monologue of the lecture-room. What can one weak individual do when the species announces to him that his time has come?

I never looked upon Ariel as merely a pupil after that. I became concerned in no impersonal or scientific way with her looks, her clothing, her language, her body; unconsciously I reached out in my turn and tried to absorb her being into mine,—not knowing then that this was a definition of love. I found myself one day, in the midst of my pedagogy, discussing with her which ribbon would better match the color of her hair. She responded to my interest, and began to care more meticulously for the hundred items that make up the beauty of a woman. She grew quieter and gentler; she anticipated my needs, and helped me at every moment with the children. Sometimes, when we gathered together for the daily story, she would sit next to me, and put a hand upon my shoulder or my arm. I became conscious of that hand as never before. It was really a pretty hand,—perfectly formed, small and delicate, and just chubby enough to be comfortable. I began to look at it stealthily and possessively.

And then one day the tide came to a flood, and all the moorings were torn away. It was after three o'clock, and the children had gone. Ariel had stayed to help me put things in order. By some fated accident our bodies touched, and my whole being was swept electrically with a current of desire. I, who had spent so many hours with the philosophers; I, who had read Schopenhauer's bitter description of women, and his disillusioning analysis of love; I, who had smiled appreciatively at every hit which the rejected Nietzsche had scored upon the subtler sex —I should have controlled myself; I should have paused and weighed circumstances; I should have considered that this was my pupil, that I was her teacher, that here was the last place in the world for love. But I caught her wildly in my arms, and kissed her hair, and her eyes, and her mouth.

She made no resistance, and no response; a strange sadness stilled her joy. It was as if she felt, in that delirious moment, what penalties she would have to pay for that embrace; how every friend and relative in the world would denounce her as a traitor to her race. And yet she was glad to give me this happiness which I was drinking from her lips. It was so innocent; how could it ever be wrong to make another happy? As for me, I knew now an intoxication such as had never come to me in the past. Fate had placed miraculously in my arms just such a girl as I had fashioned in my fantasy; I held her close to make certain it was not a dream. And I hungered and thirsted for her as if in all the world this was the woman whom nature had made for me.

"Will you forgive me, Ariel?" I whispered.

"Yes," she answered. "But I love you too."

We kissed no more that afternoon; perhaps some sense of guilt had crept within the hot consciousness of our love. As from a height I saw the widening consequences of this act; the break-up of the school; the clash of hostile races, families and creeds; the surrender of my freedom and the end of my solitude; the assumption of new tasks and new responsibilities in the world. But through it all I felt the joy of a new comradeship, an almost mystic sense of fulfilment and completion. I was content and happy to be caught up in the great web of the continuity of life. As I rode home alone I lived the scene over and over again, and saw something of its content and significance, but never with a moment of regret. I had been a fragment long enough. I would not be afraid of life. I wanted to live forward; I was glad that again all the doors were closed behind me, and that new doors and new avenues had opened in front. I have never been happier than on that afternoon. After all, what does it matter what price we pay for love?

CHAPTER VII

I EXPLORE THE HUDSON

WHAT was I to do now? I was caught in such a maze of unforeseen and chaotic circumstance that for a while I felt like letting the whole mesh and welter of things fall upon me unresisted. I would follow the path of love without looking to the right or the left, and I would let the world talk and snarl and bite. Her parents were Jewish, mine were Catholic; very well, I would do nothing about it. She was my pupil, I was her teacher, and I had done a shameful and immoral thing, subject to a thousand uncomfortable imputations; well, I would do nothing about that either. We would go off and bill and coo, and thrill and woo, and all the dogs in Christendom might howl their moralic protest unhonored and unheard. Love seemed to me so much more important than those other things, than all those other people.

That Saturday Ariel and I went to a park, and wandered all day along its brooks and across its fields. We did not talk of marriage, for that had a prosaic sound; I spoke only of the new happiness within me, and of my gratitude to her who had brought it; and Ariel told me with her girlish simplicity that she was happy too, and would go to the end of the world with me. That afternoon, however, we got no farther than Bronx Park. We sat down near a hospitable tree, whose spreading boughs sheltered us from hostile eyes, and we stayed there for hours, shoulder to shoulder, head to head, and (though not quite for hours) lips to lips. Ever since that sunny day I have honored the ritual of love.

When a week had passed I resumed the relationships and amenities of society, and acknowledged that under the supremacy of Eros there might be room for the consideration of parental and fraternal sensibilities. I decided that I would go no further without revealing everything to Ariel's mother and father, and that I would at once offer my resignation to the heads of the Freedom Association. I wrote to Ronald Dalton, and told him that having fallen in love with one of my pupils I was presumably unfit to be any longer the teacher of the school, and would relinquish my position as soon as they could find some respectable person to take my place. It was characteristic of my intoxication that I despatched this letter without considering for a moment that it would in all likelihood result in my being thrown penniless into the streets at the very time when I was preparing to become a full-fledged man. Luckily the executive committee of the Association asked me to stay till the end of the school year; and I had a chance to catch my economic breath.

CHAPTER VIII

I GO THE WAY OF ALL FLESH

On the following Monday I began my studies at Columbia. Here at last was the atmosphere I had thirsted for: the "clear, cold air of science," and the quiet surroundings of modest scholarship; the sense of human progress as resting not on politics or strife, but on silent and inconspicuous research, on the organization of inquiry and the dissemination of knowledge into every corner of the land. I drank in with delight the unassuming psychological erudition of Professor Woodworth and the brilliant biology of Professor Calkins; I watched Professor Morgan pursuing chromosomes and genes through countless generations of *Drosophila*, and for two years I followed the thorough-going courses with which that perfect teacher, Professor McGregor, initiated thousands of students into the lore of the biological laboratory. I squirmed uneasily as I took live worms and dropped them into alcohol, and shuddered as I pinned their still quivering bodies to a board and cut away their delicate skins. I pored for years into microscopes, and studied the animalcules from which, I was assured, I had been evolved. I dissected a dog-fish, a bird, a frog, and a hundred other unfortunates that had to die to make Ph.D.'s. I came away from those laboratories a little tired of malodorous carcasses, filth-filled digestive tracts, and shameless reproductive systems; but grateful nevertheless for such solid instruction as I had never had before.

And then I passed from Schermerhorn to Philosophy Hall, and found Professor Woodbridge in his prime. Of all the lecturers I heard in those four years, he was surely the ablest and most alert. I knew after one session with him that I was to enjoy the intimate self-expression of a mature and genial mind; that here was a man who had circumnavigated the intellectual globe, and could see our little problems now in that total perspective which is philosophy.

Finally I came to Professor Dewey. I smiled as I saw him cross the campus on a winter's day,—hatless and overcoatless, collar turned up and hands in his pockets, hair unsubdued and neck-tie awry; none of us would have supposed, from his bearing or his appearance, that he was the leading figure in American philosophy. Nevertheless his lectures were almost the worst in his university. His voice was a monotone and his pace an even drawl,—except when he sought Flaubertianly for the fittest word, and stared out upon the lawn till it came. Some of us went to sleep; others of us copied his lecture in longhand word for word in order to remain awake. But he was slow because he did his own thinking, and ploughed virgin soil. Most lectures are compilations; and if they flow easily on it is because they follow a beaten path. But where Dewey thought there were no paths; he had to make them as he went; and like a frontiersman he had no time for ornamental delicacies. When, in the leisure of the evening, we read over what we had taken down during the day, we discovered gold in every second line. We found that without excitement, and without exaggeration, this man was laying a firm basis, in biological psychology, for the progress of his country and his race. Sometimes he spoke so radically that only the obscurity of his speech and the modesty of his manner saved him from the sensationalism of reporters or the hunters of heresy. And then at times, with a quiet sentence of irrefutable analysis, he annihilated a theory or a movement, and brought the eager ideals of youth within the circle of reality.

I am afraid that those four years at Columbia undid me as a radical, and completed that subsidence into liberalism which had begun with my experience as a conspirator, and had been carried on by my European trip and perhaps by the retarded tempo of my blood. I had come to Columbia from the center of American anarchism, as I had come to anarchism from a seminary; and this new change, though less sharp and sudden than the first, was as fundamental and revealing. I passed from the clash of controversy to the calm of study and research, from the discussion of discordant hopes to the analysis of impartial facts. It was not that these teachers were conservative. Most of them were genuine liberals; some of them contributed to the support of the Socialist press; others had followed the career of Emma Goldman with some measure of admiration; not one of them but sympathized, and in no hypocritical way, with the aspirations of the common man.

Yet as I studied with them my Utopias moved farther back in the perspective of the future. I had thought of the world in ethical terms, and had talked of rights and wrongs; now I learned that behind rights and wrongs were desires and powers. I heard something of the impulse of mastery, and discovered that it existed as strongly in the leaders of the proletariat as in the Manufacturers' Association of America. I learned something of the acquisitive propensities of man, and saw their roots in that terrific struggle for existence, generation after generation, which had required such an instinct, which had for the most part destroyed those who lacked it, and had intensified it ruthlessly by the selection of those in whom it flourished. As long as struggle continued, and material goods remained the prime necessities of survival in the individual and in the group, that instinct to possess would continue to operate in the human soul; and Utopias that reckoned without it were compensatory castles in the air. I did not throw all my castles down, but I remade them more modestly, and nearer to the earth. I found myself fighting to keep my social faith from disintegration as I had once fought to preserve my religious belief from the assaults of this same dissolving science.

"Perhaps," I said to myself in those meditative days, "it is science, and not socialism, that will revolutionize the world. Medical science may lessen epidemics, may weaken the virulence of disease, and may teach us how to keep ourselves clean and strong. Economic science may lessen industrial tyranny by showing that when the flood of immigrant labor subsides, and contraception reduces the abundance of proletarian brawn, it will be wasteful to ruin the human resources of industry with long hours and unclean homes. Mechanical science may lessen slavery by making electric power less expensive than the muscle of the unskilled worker, and man will become only the intellectual factor in production. Historical science may rid us of superstitions, and leave us freer to understand and control the world. Psychological science may cleanse our minds of ignorance and fear, and teach us to understand and control ourselves. Perhaps these very scientists, isolated in their laboratories and silent amid the noise and argument of the rest of us, are the great changers, the great destroyers, and the great builders."

And then I asked myself, Wellsianly:

"Suppose that these scientists everywhere should realize that, united, their knowledge would be more indispensable, in war and industry, than the gold of the capitalist, the courage of the promoter, or the brawn of the proletaire? Why should they not take control of the world and make a newer Atlantis? Perhaps that would be the greatest of all revolutions!"

At that moment one of the most famous physicists of America crossed the campus. He was tall but very thin, and looked too frail for this rough world. He peered timidly through his thick glasses, and walked with his eyes upon the ground. He was evidently a sharp and subtle mind, but not a masterful man; I felt that he would run from power rather than towards it, that he would make almost any sacrifice for peace. It dawned upon me that the scientist is not a warrior and not a ruler; that the same nobility and cleanliness and modesty of soul which keep him bent obscurely over his tubes and microscopes might make him a malleable medium in the hands of men equipped at birth with the instincts of domination. Nature does not like to give two gifts to one man.

In October of that year Ariel and I were married.

After all my denunciations of free mating I found it irksome nevertheless to submit to the routine of securing a license for our love. I vowed that we would go through the formalities of the marriage ceremony with a scornful dispatch, making our required obeisance to society and the state, but flying back to our treasured privacy as soon as the formula would permit.

And so one sunny afternoon I met Ariel as she

came from the secretarial school where she was studying; and though she had her roller-skates in one hand and her books in the other, and I had a brief-case bulging with every science and a dozen philosophies, and both of us were hatless, we sallied forth to the City Hall. There we met Frank Haughwout, a Columbia associate, and his lawyer friend Harry Winter; a little later Ariel's mother came, hesitant and diffident; and together we approached the desk of the man who might legitimate our love.

"How old did you say?" he asked Ariel.

"Fifteen," she answered, fearfully. She stands before me in my memory as she stood there that day, her hair flowing down over her shoulders in schoolgirl fashion, her eyes flashing with excitement, her cheeks red with health and all a-blush with modesty, her muscular body thrilling with our great adventure.

"You're under age," said the clerk sharply. "You can't marry here without the consent of both your parents. Are they with you?"

We had known something of this, but we had had a queer hope that the clerk might have forgotten the law. Ariel's father had refused his consent; under no circumstances would he help us; indeed, had he known what we were doing he would have appeared and protested with all his soul against his daughter's apparent treachery to her people.

"The mother is here," I said, as politely as I could; "will you let her speak?"

"Perfectly useless," said the clerk; "get the father too."

We were brushed aside. Ariel had tears in her eyes, and I hot words on my tongue. But Winter quieted us.

"We'll go and see chief clerk Tully," he said.

We took an elevator to the fourth floor, and there, fortunately, was the man we sought,—bald-headed, round-faced, short, fat enough to be good-natured, and intelligent beyond the custom of public officials.

"Mr. Tully," said our lawyer, introducing me, "this new victim is a graduate student in the department of philosophy at Columbia."

I wondered at this selection of details; but Winter knew his man; philosophy was a private hobby of this master of matrimony. Tully invited me to explain my trouble; but suddenly he led me into irrelevant discourse on the current issues in science and philosophy; he found delight in leaving the dull routine of his desk for a sally into the airy world of speculation. Then he returned to earth.

"I'm forgetting what you came for," he said with a smile. "Of course you know it's against our rules to let you marry a minor without the consent of both parents."

I said nothing. I had learned that this is usually the best thing to say.

"Do you really want to marry this young lady?" he asked.

"With all my heart," I answered.

"Well," he said, "I'll take a chance on you."

He wrote a brief note, and gave it to me. We thanked him, and filed back to the clerk below. This gentleman growled at the violation of rules and precedents, but finally handed us our precious license.

"Well, if you're bound to do it, go ahead," he said, grimly.

I was quite bound. I had done all the thinking I intended to do; there has to be some cloture on thought in these matters if the race is to go on. We passed from the license-bureau down into a basement where several aldermen were marrying couples as fast as the formula could be recited. Once more we stood in line. I shuddered a little as I saw the anxious faces ahead of me—this must be a terrible thing that we were doing. And then, couple by couple, we were passed into marriage, almost as if we were buying tickets for a ball game. When our turn came I lost my head, and had to have the questions repeated and shouted at me before I could understand them. Suddenly an unforeseen question startled me:

"Where's the ring?"

"What ring?" I asked, stupefied.

"Your marriage ring, of course," shouted the awful alderman. "Do you think I can marry you without a ring?"

I had forgotten all about that damnable formality. I hated rings unreasonably as a relic of savagery, and I had never thought of them as a necessary implement of marriage. It was my modest mother-in-law who saved the day.

"Perhaps you will lend me your ring for a minute?" she whispered to the girl who had preceded Ariel to the sacrifice.

"Eh?" the girl asked. "Why should I lend you my ring, when I just got it?"

"Here's a dollar," said Ariel's mother, quietly.

"Oh," said the young lady, and handed over the ring.

The alderman frowned as I tried to fit upon Ariel's finger this borrowed bond of matrimony. But he was unwilling to be cheated of a fee which he had almost earned; and he grumbled his way through the remainder of the ceremony. "Say, 'With this ring I thee wed,' " he commanded.

I obeyed blindly.

". . . love, honor, and obey,"—I heard Ariel murmur the words, though she denies it now.

Then he handed me the certificate. We surrendered the ring, paid our fee, and rushed out into the open air, relieved and happy.

"Hurrah!" I shouted; "it's over at last." (Commencements look so much like completions.)

Ariel smiled through her tears, happy too, I hope, but fearful of the new responsibilities we were facing. Then it dawned upon me that I had not yet kissed her since our marriage. I caught her in my arms, and before the amazed hundreds that swirled around us I kissed her passionately.

"Now," I said, remembering Whitman, "shall we two stick to each other as long as we live?"

She looked up at me trustfully and resolutely.

"To the very end," she whispered.

CHAPTER IX

WANDER-YEARS

WE sought rooms near the University, but the rents there were too high, and we found ourselves forced up the hill to 136th Street. Thither we moved our combined belongings,—a bed, a typewriter, a desk, and my books. We had hired a small truck, and it was stipulated that I should have to help the driver carry our furniture three flights down from the old rooms and four flights up to our new ones. When the day's work was over I fell down upon the floor, and could hardly be persuaded to rise for the little meal which Ariel had conjured up for me out of the chaos of the kitchen. How quietly resourceful she was, how quickly and contentedly she took over the task of caring for my big appetite and our little home! Never was food sweeter to me than in those days, when we were too poor to enter a restaurant, and everything that I ate came to me from her hands, seasoned with comradeship and love.

During the day we studied at Columbia together. People stared at us, surprised to find us always arm in arm or side by side. They were not quite certain whether I was husband or brother or father, though they might have known by our tenderness that we were newly wed. Yet with all our cooing we mingled an abundance of argument; for Ariel was young and hopeful, while I, nearing thirty, felt already old and wise, and leaned to a grave moderation. Our philosophy is a function of our age of life. We pass through Utopias and idealism to knowledge and limitation as we pass through a hundred illnesses to a certain moderate health.

At Columbia once, wandering among the book-shelves, I came abruptly face to face, round a turn in the stacks, with a bent and white-haired man of perhaps some eighty years. For a moment we looked at each other with a vague hostility. "Ah," he seemed to say, "I too was once like you, eager for change, voracious of knowledge, hopeful of great achievements, and with a fretful passion for taking the world apart and putting it together again. Now I spend my hours reading the frayed yellow pages of the magazines that were popular in my youth." I felt, as I saw him moving timidly along, that given a little time and I too would look back longingly to the days of my hope and my strength, and would crawl reluctantly and fearfully towards the dark. —Another time I paused at the sight of an old man, with side-boards and Prince Albert coat, leaning on a cane and watching with awe the Mississippi of automobiles that passed the Public Library. His face showed the subtle tragedy of a man rudely left behind by a changing world. Finally he turned to an antique carriage which a precariously exalted driver had been keeping for him at the curb.

"Take me home," he said, wearily; "this confusion tires me."

Perhaps it was for the sake of such men, in mercy to them, that the mills of the gods had to grind exceeding slow.

Those days at Columbia were among the happiest of our lives. It was there that we discovered together the true City of God; not the gloomy abode of saints which the stern Augustine dreamed of, but that fair and pleasant Country of the Mind where all the great dead are still alive, and wisdom makes with beauty an eternal music. We saw Plato there, still handsome in his eighty years, telling his students of the perfect state; and grave Euripides writing his mournful tragedies in his cottage near the sea at Salamis; we stood beside Praxiteles as he carved the tender likeness of Aphrodite for the Cnidians; we followed Dante as he wandered through Hell and Purgatory seeking Beatrice; we drank and laughed with Rabelais in the Abbey of Thélème, and heard the merry quips of Shakespeare and rare Ben at the Mermaid Inn; we suffered in prison with Verlaine, and lay on the grass, on a transparent summer morning, while the poet sang to us of the life-long love of comrades. We were filled with a strange and quiet happiness when we thought that the geniuses of every land and every age stood always ready to walk

that sent Woodrow Wilson, the pacifist, to war. I did my best to understand the motives of a course that seemed to me drenched in treachery. The President's ancestry and culture and traditions were British; he confessed frankly enough, when the battle was over, that no matter how little formal cause had been given, he would have asked for war whenever it seemed that the Allies, without us, would be destroyed. He was accustomed to an English universe; he could not bear the thought of Teutons bestriding a Prussianized world. That he sent our young men to death to secure the loans of our bankers to European governments, or to ensure American domination of South American finance and trade, was a hyper-Marxian conception which I was too tender-minded to entertain. I liked Woodrow Wilson's prose too well to believe him capable of such brutality. And even to this day, somehow, I have an affection for the man.

I thought he was grievously mistaken in going to war, though God knows I thought so with some measure of humility. I had learned my lesson by that time, and could conceive the possibility of my being wrong. I was filled with awe as I contemplated the complexities of statesmanship; how could I, in the midst of a hundred other concerns, and still adolescent mentally, understand the secret factors that determined international events? And I too preferred—perhaps through time's irrational habituation, and the accidents of place—a British to a German world; like all my tribe I thought the educated Englishman the finest gentleman on earth. But I could not believe that England, which was sending so many troops to capture Asiatic soil, would be defeated unless we sent our happy youth to her aid; it seemed to me that the effect was as if we had dispatched our troops to the East to win for this crafty Lion the oil and wheat of Mesopotamia. Nor could I forget that England had loved Kitchener on account of his ferocity, that she had her own sorry list of swashbucklers, fire-eaters, and tyrants, and her crimes of black oppression in distant lands,—crimes muffled, for our ears, by the intervening seas. Was the difference between these German cousins so great as to warrant the forcible alienation of the American people from their age-long loyalty to peace, and the surrender of our moral meaning in a world that might have begun to unlearn war if we had shown that a great nation could live without it?

They told me that peace would be cowardice; but was not our war itself a conscripted cowardice? Was there any glory in a victory enforced by fear of the artillery behind us? Yes, the volunteers had courage: I saluted them; they were brave. But we others, who found mothers to support, or married in haste, in order to evade the draft; and those lofty ones who sat comfortably in their office chairs and spoke or wrote of glory—was that bravery?

I thought the better courage would have been the courage to be ourselves. I thought, as the Presi-

to give these sons to death. Harry came back; but how many there were who never returned, or returned maimed in body and mind, or coarsened forever by the filth and brutality of war?

I see twenty million corpses strewing a thousand battlefields. I know with what despair they went to war, and how loath they were to kill. I hear them praying to their gods, as they advance with drawn bayonets and broken hearts, that they may be spared from murder and from death. And then I see them crazed with the passion of strife and slaughter; snarling and crying out with hatred and fear; sending a bullet into this lad's head, pushing the sharp bayonet into that lad's breast; rushing on over the crumpled body of the fallen foe; stepping perhaps upon the quivering and bloodied face that some mother once admired; then stumbling for a little moment, and looking up too late; feeling the cold blade entering the body, twisting and tearing the vitals; falling under the onrush of battle, under a thousand heels impinging cruelly, again and again, on every muscle and bone, on nose and eyes and mouth; remembering in one brief flash a thousand happy days of far-off youth; then hearing great hammer strokes upon the brain; moaning and asking heaven why these things should be; struggling, struggling, to keep one little bit of life from the universal conqueror; tiring, yielding, sighing out the last hope with the last breath; and sinking down heavily, under a thousand stifling weights, into the darkness and futility of death. That is how they died, those twenty million men.

And then peace came, more suddenly than the war. Shall I ever forget that first Armistice Day, when all America came out of her madness and sorrow to blow the trumpets and sing the songs of peace? Did we not parade all night, unwearied, covering ourselves joyfully with streaming bonds of brotherhood renewed, and greeting with tears the long-awaited dawn? Your soul was revealed on that day, my country; never had you celebrated war as then you celebrated peace. And it was not your victory that you sang; no lust of bloody triumph coarsened your voice, or darkened your shining eyes; you beat and pounded for peace, you knew her holiness once more; you were glad that now you could raise your hand in fellowship to the world, and not to kill. That night you knew happiness again.

But in a door-way on Lexington Avenue I saw a woman weeping.

"Why are you crying?" I asked. "Don't you know that the war is over, and that we are all friends again?"

"Yes," she said, and her voice broke out into a bitter wail. "But it's too late, too late."

"Have you lost one of your boys in the war?"

"My only boy," she whispered. "They told me

yesterday. O my boy, my George, you'll never come back to me, you'll never come back to me."

As I bent over to comfort her I saw a hundred thousand mothers, everywhere in America, standing or sitting in doorways or at windows, looking dull-eyed and empty-hearted on our joy, and waiting for the sons whom their arms would never hold again.

CHAPTER XI

I PLAY POLITICS

One would imagine that by this time I had become sufficiently disillusioned to retire into a studious corner, and protect myself, as far as might be, from the harsh contacts and bubble-bursting pricks of life. One would suppose, at the very least, that I had come to understand the futility of an intellectual plunging into the labyrinths and shady catacombs of politics. But my scepticism and rationalism have always been matters of the head, that never crossed the medulla into the deeper roots of my behavior and my being. At bottom I am as romantic and sentimental as a high-school girl or an old maid. I think I shall never grow up.

So it was that in 1919, still burning with hatred of war, I accepted the invitation of some friends to join them in the high and mighty game of making a new political party. It seemed a comparatively simple matter: Providence had arranged everything for us; we had only to reach out our hands and take the fruits of office. Was not America secretly resentful of having been dragooned into the war? Were not the Republican powers attacking Woodrow Wilson with a campaign of vilification unprecedented since the days of Abraham Lincoln? The Democratic Party might be destroyed, in this election, beyond any possibility of resurrection. As to the Republicans, had they not joined in the war-making as merrily as any Democrat? And were they not on the verge of nominating a Prussian general as their candidate for the presidency? Here was our opportunity, if ever opportunity would come, to gather together the scattered and shattered forces of the old Americanism and the new progressivism; to bind them into a party, and offer to the people the chance they had been longing for—to vote for peace and freedom. "America waits," we said. We never dreamed how long America would wait.

It was J. A. H. Hopkins who brought us together. I always liked everything about him except the initials. To begin with, he was the handsomest man in America. I was convinced that if he would only let us nominate him for the presidency half the population would vote for him on his face value. And he not only looked like a gentleman, he behaved like one. All who met him wanted to do anything he asked. Even his relatives liked him. He had left a remunerative business in order to give all his time, and nearly all his savings, to the work of establishing a third party. He burned with a tenacious idealism that never lost hope or acknowledged defeat; we might come to our meetings with him despondent to the point of cynicism, but in a moment he was carrying us along enthusiastically towards Utopia. No man could be a pessimist about America after knowing "Hop."

We met in a little office in East Fortieth Street, and laid our plans like breathless conspirators. At that first meeting, if I may trust my memory, there were, besides Hopkins and myself, Allen McCurdy, McAlister Coleman and Arthur Hays. It was arranged that we should write a "Call to Americans," inviting liberals throughout the country to send us in their dollars and their names. We received more names than dollars, but we were encouraged to go on. Our executive committee grew to ponderous proportions, and our meetings took on the dignity of a movement to save America. I thrilled once more with the enthusiasm of younger days. Something of the warm faith which had burned within me for religion flamed up again as I thought of the new era that our great crusade might usher in. It was the final fire of my old idealism; if this too should flicker out and die, nothing would be left to me but a cynical and crabbed age. It was the last fling of my youth.

We might have learned from our own behavior, and from our own turbulent debates, how impotently divided American progressives were. The younger ones among us argued for co-operation with the Socialists and the new "Farmer-Labor Party"; the older heads, like George Record and Amos Pinchot, believed that it would be wiser to work alone, and

platform. The labor leaders frowned, and tried to continue with the discussion then holding the floor. But the convention had a soft spot in its heart for the man who had dared to love peace when all others had lauded war; and they greeted the picture with wild approval. Then the delegates from Wisconsin lifted their state banner on high and marched out into the aisle, singing, over and over again, "We want LaFollette, we want LaFollette!"

"Order!" cried the chairman. "You're out of order. Sit down!"

But they would not sit down; and the noise of his gavel could not drown their songs. We delegates from New York raised our banner and followed them, and others followed us, until there were sixteen states in line. Round and round we marched, shouting and singing like typical Americans drunk with the enthusiasm of politics. We tried to get other states to fall in with us; but their labor delegations were too strong; they clung resolutely to their banners, and waited for the orders of their chiefs. Half an hour later we were all seated again, and the Committee on Resolutions and Platform reported to the convention. Our motion that we should first vote on candidates was defeated. I learned that parades have as much importance in conventions as elections have in determining the policy of governments.

The majority report proposed a socialist platform calling for the nationalization of the larger industries. The minority report, read by George Record, was the platform which Senator LaFollette himself had signed. It was more moderate than the other, of course; but it represented a point of view far beyond that which the mind of America had reached. We knew that our whole fate rested on the acceptance of that minority report.

We stinted no energy in our forlorn effort to stem the tide. Pinchot pled with the convention, in his quiet aristocratic way, not to adopt a class platform. Was there not such a platform already in the field, offered to America with all the eloquence of an imprisoned leader? People did not identify themselves, in America, with the class to which they belonged, but with that to which they aspired, and whose dress and thought they loved to imitate. Record pleaded with these new statesmen to accept counsel of men who had had many years of experience in public affairs, and knew the temper of the country. Americans had a natural distrust of platforms that proposed to rewrite at one stroke the entire political and economic constitution of the land; like Sancho they preferred an island in the Mediterranean to a continent in Utopia. Hopkins pleaded with them for a cleansing away of their hot emotions and their personal resentments. I pleaded with them, with passionate and ridiculous futility. But they would not hear us. The labor leaders had passed the word that their candidate was not LaFollette, and their followers followed them. In the center of the hall sat the Illinois delegation, numbering three hundred men—

one-fourth of all the delegates; they were unanimous against us, and drowned out our oratory mercilessly with their noise. It was not a convention, it was a mob. The chairman acted honestly; he did his best to secure us a hearing, but they would not give it to us. Our substitute resolution embodying the minority platform was voted down.

After that it did not matter what happened. Our defeated leaders sat back exhausted, and said no more. Amos Pinchot, having fought to the last inch, lay limp across two chairs, sleeping so soundly that not all the pandemonium of the balloting convention could awaken him. I found my way back to the Morrison, and went to bed.

In the morning I learned the dénouement. Senator LaFollette had refused to allow his name to be included among the nominations. Then the labor leaders, mostly Irish Catholics, had named a young Irish Catholic lawyer from New York, a man of attractive personality and a matchless orator. His rivals for the nomination sent word around the hall that he was a Catholic. At once the convention ceased to be a political gathering and became a religious meeting, hotly divided according to their ancient faiths. Early in the balloting it became clear that no Catholic could receive the nomination. The young lawyer withdrew his name, and the convention faced the pathetic anti-climax of looking about for a man who would condescend to accept its honors. For hours they talked and waited and voted; and then at last, towards dawn, in order to go home and sleep, they nominated a man whom nobody had ever heard of before, and whom no one will ever hear of again.

That is how I played politics in Chicago.

On the train back to New York I was accosted by a well-dressed, comfortable-looking man, ruddy-faced and gray-haired, with a twinkle in his eye.

"You'll pardon my asking, but aren't you the young man who spoke at the Labor Party Convention yesterday?"

I was more offended at being called a young man than I would be now; people do not call me that any longer.

"Yes," I said, briefly, not anxious to review that ignominy.

"Well, you were right, of course," he said, making himself at home in the opposite seat. "But how in the world did you ever get mixed up with that wild gang?"

"I thought I could be a lion-tamer," I answered, sadly.

He laughed the hearty laugh of a successful man.

"I was passing the place by chance yesterday; I went in because the noise aroused my curiosity. Those labor delegates reminded me of the time when I belonged to the Knights of Labor, 'way back in the nineties."

I began to be interested. This prosperous business man had been a laborer? I should never have suspected it.

"So there were labor unions then too," I remarked. "Were they as radical as Chicago's?"

"Oh, yes," he said. "There's always been about the same proportion of radicals in this country, and perhaps in most countries, since I was born. When radical parties grow, like the Socialists in Germany, or the Laborites in England, it's not because the people are becoming more radical, but because the radical party is becoming comparatively conservative."

"So you think we make no progress?"

"I wouldn't say that. We make all sorts of progress—except in government. And after all, government is unimportant; it's the economic life that counts; that's where mastery lies, and that's where oppression really hurts. Real men go into business, and leave politics to those who don't know better. Hence the progress in politics."

I said nothing; but he was content to carry on the conversation.

"I was a Socialist once myself," he said. "I sympathize with these young radicals, but I know what will happen to them. I'm an awful example. Either they'll succeed materially, or they won't. If they don't they'll continue to complain about 'the environment,' or 'the sins of society,'—they'll plead 'not guilty,' as we used to do in Blatchford's days. But if they learn the ropes and get on you won't see their names in the Socialist membership books any more. Ten years later they'll be voting for the most conservative candidate in the field, on the ground that they would lose money by any disturbance or uncertainty in business conditions. This leakage of ability from the radical movement goes on all the time; the cream rises to the top and gets skimmed away. About the only clever fellows who remain are those who hold positions of honor or leadership. That's why you have so many radical parties; there are more offices to go around."

"I think there are some who are loyal under all conditions," I said.

He smiled.

"They are holy exceptions who can be counted on two hands."

I was silent, too tired and apathetic to make argument. But he went on.

"You see, every radical is a rebel, and every socialist is an individualist. Now you can't organize individualists. They split into a thousand sects, just as individualist Protestantism does. Everyone wants to have his way. There's no possible discipline among them. When one of them is outvoted he goes off in a huff and starts a new party. At last there are so many sects that nobody takes them seriously, and the big fellows who run the country can safely leave them to fight one another to death."

He puffed his cigar, and I looked out of the window moodily. He resumed.

"It might be different if radicals didn't marry. A radical married is already half a conservative. The family is naturally a conservative institution. When you're afraid, you're conservative; and parents are always worried about the future of their children. Nobody is so selfish, as far as the rest of the world is concerned, as the mother who loves her offspring. When the parents begin to save, their radicalism evaporates. Even if they have only a few hundred dollars put aside for a rainy day they are suspicious of any movement that wants to turn things inside out. They don't want any bank failures, much less a government overturn that might make their little savings as worthless as Russian rubles."

"It all sounds very hopeless," I remarked. "And yet you said you believed in progress."

"Why not? You're thinking of something to be gotten by passing laws. It doesn't come that way. Voting is just a modern sport, and means about as much in its results to the country as a world-series ball-game. Wealth will go on ruling, whether we vote or not."

"I don't agree with you," I said.

"Well," he asked, with the good nature of a man smoking a satisfactory cigar, "what do you think?"

I did not want to think, but I tried in my weak way to answer him.

"I think knowledge will rule. To-day it is commercial knowledge that rules—the ability to sell things to people who do not need them. The rich are no longer those who make things, but those who buy and sell things. That won't go on forever."

He smiled patiently.

"Yes?" he suggested.

"A higher knowledge will come. Scientific knowledge. It has come in war; there already the business man's type of knowledge is worthless; it only makes for chaos and corruption, as in our shipping and aviation scandals. Some day science will be applied as far in industry as it is in war; and a knowledge of mathematics, physics, chemistry, engineering, statistics, biology, psychology, and similar fields will be in greater demand, with almost every firm, than the knowledge of where to buy cheap and how to sell dear. Capital without science will be useless, labor without science will be useless. Labor as we know it, manual labor, will disappear. Electricity—clean hydro-electric or aero-electric power—will do the menial work of the world. There'll be no 'working class' at all. There'll be no slums, no poverty, no dirt in the world any more."

"You inspire me," he said, with genial irony. "I suspect it won't come in my time; but in any case it would be better than a bloody revolution."

"There have been only two revolutions," I said, "—the agricultural and the industrial. The third will be the scientific revolution. It will be the greatest and most peaceful of all. Slavery will pass away, and knowledge will rule."

He smiled again, almost tenderly.

"I congratulate you," he said; "you are still young."

CHAPTER XII

NADIR

THAT conversation, dear Reader, was merely an invention of my imagination; I have not the heart to deceive you. And that vague and tenuous business man was only another side of myself, one of the many selves that made me the stage of a bitter debate as I returned from Chicago and politics to life and home. I hesitate to confess the depths of despair, cynicism, and apathy to which I fell in those days. At times I classed all men under various species of villainy; all officeholders were corrupt, all trade-union leaders were politicians, all business men were misers, all conservatives were cowards, and all radicals were fools.

I began to see history as a kaleidoscope of stagnation. The more life had changed, the more it had remained the same. There had been hundreds of political revolutions, and not one of them but had begotten a new ruling class as corrupt and ruthless as the old. Every invention had been captured by the strong, and had increased the gap between them and the weak. The development of machinery had made millionaires of the few, and mere animate tools of the many. The development of transportation had begotten a class of middlemen who absorbed, to the point of diminishing returns, the results of the farmer's husbandry and the proletarian's industry; men rose to position and opulence not by producing consumable goods but by interposing themselves inescapably between producer and consumer; the arteries of the world's economic life were being squeezed tighter and drier every year. The development of communication—of printing and telegraph and telephone and wireless—had merely increased the facilities for spreading misinformation, prejudice, and propaganda; in time of stress these agencies were no longer media for news, but instruments of "morale"; and at all times they served as a vast mechanism of suggestion so irresistible through unanimity and volume that not one person in a thousand could do anything else but think and feel with the crowd. The development of science had made explosives, long-distance artillery, and air-plane bombers, which put subject nations and subject majorities absolutely at the mercy of vigorous governments and imperialist powers. The discovery of the means of contraception had resulted in the sterility of the intelligent and the multiple fertility of the unfortunate; it had nullified the work of education by destroying the social transmission of moral and intellectual culture; and it was gradually repeopling Europe and America with a population reconciled to slavery and wedded to bigotry and superstition.

In this frame of mind I saw nothing in democracy but mockery; a quadrennial or biennial drama which the rulers staged for the ruled as a substitute for the circuses that had soothed the proletariat of Rome. In America the economic bases of democracy —free land, free competition, and open opportunity —had almost passed away; the tools of production had become so complex and costly that only great corporations could purchase them; the differentiation of trades, the growth of land values, and the accumulation of hereditary privileges had multiplied a hundredfold the natural inequality of men; and the specious equality of the vote was the last rag with which America could cover her industrial feudalism and present a virtuously democratic front to the world. And that surviving pretense of letting the people rule had melted away in the heat of the very war that was to confer democracy upon all the nations of the earth.

From complaining that democracy had disappeared, I passed to the inconsistent view that it was a worthless and impossible scheme in any case. I reflected on the growing complexity of political affairs; the transition from the easy-going ceremonial existence of medieval courts, ruling, with the aid of the priesthood, a homogeneous population of peasants, to the harassed life of a modern government, caught in a maze of foreign relations, and called upon at every turn to adjudicate among the conflicting forces of an individualist industrial society. How could that poor abstraction, the average citizen, pretend to have the knowledge requisite for forming, on these entangled issues, any judgment that would be worth expressing? It was only by courteous hypocrisy that the men who decided these issues went through the occasional formality of consulting the nation. And the unreality of the franchise was no greater in the politics of the country than in the affairs of labor unions, or of radical parties; everywhere a few men who had knowledge and ability led by the nose a majority who had none. I concluded that elections were an irksome and expensive futility, and that we ought to ask our masters to rule us without adding to our burdens of indirect taxation the immense cost of these periodical orgies of national delusion.

I tried to comfort myself with the trite consideration that an uninformed electorate might nevertheless choose representatives who, gathered in conference, would meet with fair adequacy the problem of reconciling the brute realities of economic strife with the desires of their constituents. For a time, in Washington, I studied our National Palaver from the Senate galleries; and I discovered very soon that these splendid orators had never been selected for their economic knowledge, or their administrative competence. It was a scandal known to all the world that these congresses and parliaments had been snubbed most cavalierly during and since the War; that the executive power had encroached upon the legislature till the latter had become merely a talk-shop and a register of imperial or presidential decrees. I found that the concentration of economic power had begotten, as its natural heir, a concentration of political power; that state rights were dead; that the business of the world now got itself done through cabinets and councils and expert economic boards; that those very representatives whom we so labored to elect, whom we had prided ourselves on as the obedient voices of our sovereign will,—these representatives, too, counted for nothing, except as voices, capable of endless eloquence, but to no end.

In those dark days I shed most of the social and political ideals that had exhilarated me in my twenties. I, who had dreamed of the time when the workers would rule the world, now found it unpleasant to ride alongside them in the subway. I lost whatever enthusiasm I might ever have had for a dictatorship of the proletariat, or even for "the rule of the people." Socialism, like Christianity, would always be a voice in the wilderness crying out for justice and brotherly love, while the world would go on with the struggle for existence and the survival of the "fittest"—that is to say, the most acquisitive, the most pugnacious, and the most masterful. There would always be strong and weak, clever and simple, ruthless and timid men; and the ruthlessly clever strong would always rule the timid and simple weak. Material comforts would increase; but political changes would be at best a transition between two forms of oligarchical power. It might be an oligarchy of land-owners, as in the Middle Ages; or an oligarchy of industrial and financial magnates, as in the current world; or an oligarchy of trade-union leaders, such as could conceivably come in the England of 1950. But an aristocracy of some kind was inevitable. Why should I disturb myself as to just which minority would rule or exploit the world when I should be long since dead? I no longer cared.

No; all these ideals of mine, all the ideals of mankind, were the cowardly self-deceptions with which we covered up the sharp actualities of life. Socialism was envy; anarchism was a secret lust for power; democracy was an anesthetic applied to the people while their pockets were being picked and their blood was sucked away. Love was the desire for possession, courtship was combat, mating was mastery, marriage was monotony, parentage was the subjugation of the individual by the race. The family was an incorporated selfishness, maternal love was a proprietary instinct, kindness was a timid bribe to peace. Christianity was a lovely phrase designed to conceal the war of each against all; religion was merely the fear of death, and the egotistic hunger for perpetuity.

Behind all these fig-leaves lay the naked truth of the struggle for existence, for food and mates and land and power. That struggle had always gone on: the sharp relics of the caves showed how it had filled the lives of Neanderthal and Cro-Magnon men; the

Homeric ballads wove into one song the lust for women and for conquest; beneath the exalted culture of Athens lay a chaotic individualism and a barbarous slavery; history was the Newgate Calendar of nations, a record of war and slaughter, of robbery and deceit, of crime and exploitation, of ignorance and bigotry and suicidal vice. And there was no sign that the future would be different from the past. Population would continue to press upon the means of subsistence, filling up the inviting spaces of the world like water running into pools, and fighting with stealthy mercilessness for the insufficient resources and luxuries of the earth. There would be greater and more marvelous machines than before; but they would enslave and brutalize the masses, and in every generation they would destroy millions in the holocausts of war. If, in all this hell of violence and greed, an individual or a people should try to realize the ideals of brotherhood and peace, they would be crushed down into vassalage by men and races unscrupulously strong. The very requirements of the struggle for existence would force men to be grasping warriors. Undoubtedly the time would come when some hardier and more cunning animal would conquer and enslave or destroy mankind; or perhaps some persistent insect, or the multiplying bacteria, would at last capture the citadel they had so long besieged, and bring man to an end with pestilence. And then these species too would live and struggle, and meet superior foes, and these again; until the heat or energy of earth and sun would fail, and life in every form would perish from a planet inhospitably cold and dead. Evolution was not progress, it was war; and its end was not Utopia, but death.

I wonder how many men and women were passing through a similar disillusionment in those days; for how many of them the world of hope and faith faded away, revealing for the first time the stark reality and cruelty of life? I believe that there were thousands and thousands of people who could have matched all my despair with theirs, thousands who like me had gone through the double bereavement and the double apostasy of leaving the faith of their fathers and the hopeful visions of their youth. I met them everywhere as I passed through America; I would have met them in Europe had I gone there again. The War had broken the hearts or the hopes of millions who had once felt the fire of social passion burning in their blood. The Russian Revolution had roused in some souls the most fantastic expectations; and when it became clear that the Revolution could not realize their dreams, those who had been most enthusiastic became most cynical. An undertow of pessimism seemed to be dragging the finest, and once the most fervent, souls into a maelstrom of cynicism and despair. Everything had been tried, the most superhuman efforts had been made; but every effort had failed. There was hardly anything left to do, except perhaps, if one could, to eat and drink and be merry while it was day. For the night would come, after which there would be nothing.

I think it was about this time that I became conscious of the sombre reality and quiet certainty of death. I was thirty-five now; and probably the sense that youth and energy were slipping from me had much to do with the loss of my earlier ideals and hopes. I no longer felt the exhilarating surplus of vital income over vital expenditure; every day I used up more power than I could regain. In youth I had been always on the move, excitable, energetic, hasty; now the pace of life slackened in me, and I observed how at every turn I sought to save my strength.

I began to understand the look of fear in the eyes of the old; their lack of interest in the struggles of the world; their long silences and broodings: they had seen the advancing shadow of the Enemy. I began to hear of the death of vigorous men whom I had known in my youth; even of playmates who must have been yet in the prime of life. What futile transitory things we were! Men and women were falling dead around me almost as if we were in advancing battle-line and a thousand shells were decimating us. It dawned upon me at last that I too would die, I who so loved the sun and the green fields and the touch of love and the laughter of children—I would have to leave them, and go down like all the rest into everlasting darkness. Once I stood in the doorway of the New Old South Church in Boston, and read the memorial to its ancient founders. They were two hundred and fifty years dead; and yet they too had been young and strong, full of enthusiasm and ambition, unthinking of the end. How pitiless time is! How every life must pass away, though all the world else continues, careless of our going! Time is our greatest benefactor and our greatest foe—it gives us wisdom and it gives us death. Not death itself is terrible, but leaving undone the things we might do, and leaving behind us forever the souls we have learned to love.

I tried to believe, but I could not believe, that there would be another life for me after this weakening frame should break. What a consolation religion must be, I thought, to all those who see death! I might have faced the matter more cheerfully had I not known in childhood that relieving hope. It had gone from me, and nothing had taken its place; I was left empty and desolate. I belonged to the age of the Great Sadness. They had told me a pretty story when I was young, and now I would always mourn because that story was not true. All man's hopes were false; all things would die; and every heart must break.

CHAPTER XIII

I BECOME A DADDY

AND then Ethel came.

That, though it is here so near the end, was the center and turning-point of my life. For many years Ariel and I had pondered the pros and cons of parentage. We lived in the age and place of the emancipated woman; and the reasonable revolt which had broken out against the mechanical fertility of the old-fashioned wife had passed over into an extreme reaction in which childlessness was the sign of a liberated mind. We had participated in the birth-control movement, and had known its leaders well. We had heard a thousand times of the dangers and tribulations that came with children; we had never been told of the joys they might bring. We took it for granted that discretion was the better part of love.

While we had been growing up, the Industrial Revolution had played many a prank with the happiness of women. It had brought about such changes in their status, their habits, and their minds as rivaled in rapidity the industrial transition itself. It had lured them from the varied drudgery of the home into the dull routine of the factory, merely solacing their slavery with wages. No doubt the first feminine pay-envelope was almost as exhilarating as the first sin. It seemed to bring emancipation at last from the brutal tyranny of the male. That it was another writ of bondage could not appear on that first bright day of freedom. And so one by one the women of our great cities had been drawn into offices and factories by the terrific suction of that economic law which impels all but the finest employers to seek the cheapest labor to produce the cheapest goods.

Ariel had barely known this serfdom of the shop; but even that brief glimpse had frightened her. We thought that she had escaped the evils of the new order; but very soon we found that no woman could save herself from them entirely. For the same industrial expansion which had forced women into the factories had stolen from the home the hundred occupations which had filled the life of women in the past. One after another the old domestic industries had disappeared: the machines of the shop could sew and wash and iron and clean and cook more cheaply than the unaided mother in the home. Nothing was left of the home but a house, and then an apartment or cell in a gigantic hive; and above the proletariat nothing was left of woman but her beauty and her sex. She had no children and she had no work. She had lost her function, and therefore her significance and her happiness; her "emancipation" had made her, unwittingly and unwillingly, a hundred times more parasitic than before. It was brave of her to go into the factory; she sought there the work and meaning that had gone from her; she did not care to remain a functionless ornament, a thing of beauty that would not be a joy forever.

I had been reared by a generation which held it disgraceful that a man should let his wife work outside the home—though it had said nothing of slavery within. That feeling too is caught in the flux of transition, and will shortly pass away. But so it was with me; and in consequence Ariel found herself aimlessly idle, consumed with a sense that her life was incomplete, and her happiness unsubstantial and insecure. This feeling of emptiness and dissatisfaction entered even into me, absorbed though I was in a hundred tasks. I began to be jealous of certain friends of mine whose faces beamed as they looked upon their children. I did not dare speak to Ariel of so old-fashioned and sentimental a yearning; I knew that in this matter she would bear the brunt of the risk and the suffering, and that hers was the right to choose. But one night as we sat in the dark, her arm around my neck and mine about her waist, we told each other of our discontent, and I hinted vaguely at what I thought might be the solution. For a time Ariel said nothing. And then, as my lips wandered over her hair, she whispered her consent.

It was an index of the times that before making this final step into the fulness of life we went to a famous physician and asked him to examine into our fitness for parentage. Were we quite worthy to participate in the reproduction of the race? We took the question very much to heart, and trembled a little as we were put through the tests. The good Doctor decided that the race might take a chance on us, and we walked out with our heads up and our souls elated with this new adventure. I was already proud in presumptuous anticipation of the most common of human achievements, and the most minor of male rôles.

There was a subtle pride too in Ariel's carriage when, a few months later, she knew that she would be a mother. She felt none of the shame that some superlatively modern women have, who hide within four doors, and starve their double selves of air and movement to cover up the crime of pregnancy. Ariel marched forth bravely, and took the sun from morn till night, resolved that her child should have the best start that healthy motherhood could give it. And as I watched her the eternally youthful blood of the race began to course mysteriously through my veins again; I forgot that I was passing the peak of the hill of life, and that love is a prelude to death and replacement; instead, a strange new happiness began to crowd out my political disillusionment and my philosophical despair.

How carefully we counted the days, and prepared

ourselves for the great fulfilment! What discussions we carried on about every article of diet and every habit of life! We sought out the physician of best repute in our locality, and Ariel went to him regularly. It never entered our innocent heads that his examinations were superficial and careless, and that with all our preparations we were sailing into disaster.

We calculated that on Monday, May 12th, the little wonder would mature. About eleven o'clock on Saturday evening Ariel complained of a severe headache; and at once we suspected that the great ordeal had begun. I called up our doctor and begged him to come over. He laughed at me.

"Only a headache? Anybody can get a headache. There's plenty of time yet. You wouldn't want me to come and sit around just for a headache, would you? Give your wife some aspirin tablets."

The truth was that the villain was going to bed, and did not want to be disturbed, even for the sake of the species. I let him be, and gave Ariel what headache tablets we had in the house. We were alone; and there was no friend in the other apartments whom we could ask to run errands for us at that time of the night. The headache continued, and became worse.

"Oh, Jack, there's a great hammer pounding in on my brain," Ariel moaned. "Can't you get that doctor to come? I'm so afraid."

Suddenly her eyes closed, her face whitened, her

body stiffened out on the couch where she had been reclining, and her hands began to paw the air as if fighting off some enemy. I was horrified.

"Ariel, Ariel, what's the matter?" I cried, catching her in my arms. But she did not hear me, and her hands passed aimlessly over my face. Her knees rose convulsively and her head fell back. Then slowly her body relaxed, her limbs straightened, and her hands ceased their wild movement; she seemed to be sleeping.

I rushed again to the telephone, and asked for my doctor's number. I heard his bell ring, but there was no response.

"Ring till he answers," I begged the operator. And at last he spoke.

"Oh," he said, sleepily, "is that you?"

I told him of the convulsion Ariel had had.

"That's bad," he said. "I'll come over at once. Meanwhile call up Fordham Hospital and ask them to come and get your wife. It will be too much for me."

It was an hour before he came. In the meantime I sat beside my sleeping Ariel, anxious as I have never been before or since; praying incoherently that her suffering would be brief, that there would be no more convulsions, and that the doctor would come. Suddenly Ariel opened her eyes, and looked at me wildly.

"Oh, God!" she cried, "I can't bear it. Didn't you get the doctor?"

"Yes, sweetheart," I answered, ashamed; "he's coming. Where does it hurt?"

"In my head," she said, weakly. And then again her eyes closed, her knees jumped up, her mouth bubbled with froth, and her hands moved wildly through the air. I did not know what to do; I put my arms around her and tried to hold her still, though I knew that that would do no good. In those moments I forgot my religious doubts, and called upon God over and over again to come to our aid, and not to let my Ariel die. And then once more she fell back exhausted, and slept.

The doctor came, evidently tired and resentful. He tried the pulse, listened to the heart, took the temperature, and did other learned and traditional things. Ariel did not awake.

"Has she had any abdominal pains yet?" he asked.

"No," I replied; "at least she claims the pain is in her head."

"Well, she ought to know. If there are no abdominal pains it will be a long time before she is ready. Have you called up the hospital?"

"Yes. They said they'd be here soon."

"They will; they're reliable."

And then, despite my protests, he left us.

It was about two o'clock in the morning when he went. At five o'clock the ambulance came. During those three hours Ariel had convulsions every quarter of an hour, with increasing violence. When the young hospital doctor appeared I saw at once from his face that the situation was grave.

"It's an eclampsia case," he said. "It will be troublesome, but she ought to pull through."

"Do most such cases come out all right?" I asked, anxiously.

"About fifty per cent of them," he replied.

So Ariel had one chance out of two for her life.

I helped them place her on a stretcher, and led the way carefully as the doctor and his aides carried her down the stairs. When they had laid her in the ambulance I asked might I ride with them to the hospital.

"No," the doctor said, decisively; "we're absolutely forbidden to let any one ride with us."

"I'll just ride on the tail-board," I pleaded.

"We can't do it. Take the trolley at the foot of the hill, and you'll get there as soon as we will."

I looked at Ariel as if I would never see her again, and then rushed down the hill. There were no trolleys visible anywhere, nor any taxicabs. I was a mile and a half from the hospital. I began to walk, looking back for a trolley or a cab; but when none appeared I broke into a run. I burst into the hospital with a minimum of formality.

"Where have they taken my wife?" I asked of the first nurse I saw,—as if all the world knew Ariel.

"I don't know," she answered, patiently. "But they just brought in a 'clampsia case; is that it?

I think they've gone to Ward Three; on the second floor, at that end."

I rushed up the stairs, and to Ward Three. I found Ariel in the midst of a violent convulsion; two doctors held her lest she should fall to the floor, or hurt herself against the iron bed. One of them greeted me.

"I'm Nelson, one of your old students at The Workers' Church. So is Dr. Cox. You may trust us to do the very best we can for your wife. We've already sent for Dr. Telfaer, who is our consulting specialist in these cases."

"But will she come through?" I asked, in a breaking voice.

"I think so," he said.

They were ominous words for me; and though Ariel had again fallen back into an exhausted sleep, I trembled to think that at any moment she might have another convulsion.

"Will you step into the waiting-room for a few minutes?" Dr. Cox suggested.

I obeyed, anxious to keep their good will; but I feared they were about to do some terrible thing to Ariel. Ten minutes later they called me back.

"We took some blood from her," said Dr. Cox. "She had a very high blood-pressure. Now the convulsions won't be so violent."

I nearly embraced him for this crumb of comfort. Just then poor Ariel drew herself up into a heap, and moaned, and pawed the air blindly again.

The doctors held her hands gently, and one of them slipped a bit of wood between her teeth lest she should bite her tongue.

"Who was your physician?" asked Dr. Nelson.

I named the scoundrel.

"He neglected her criminally. Any honest examination would have shown excess albumin, and it could have been remedied. He ought to be run out of the profession."

Ariel was quiet now, and seemed to me to be sleeping more peacefully and breathing more easily than before. I had time to notice the patient on the cot beside her. She was tossing about restlessly, though her eyes were closed; and she moaned without ceasing.

"Is she in childbirth pains?" I asked Dr. Cox.

"Yes. She's another eclampsia case. We shall have to operate on her to-day."

"What sort of operation?"

"Cæsarian."

I could say no more. I knew that they might have to do that to Ariel,—cut her dear body open, and take out our child, leaving perhaps both of them dead. A dull and suffocating heat spread through me and consumed my strength. I sat down on the nurse's chair near Ariel's bed, and looked blindly at the floor. Why had I been so anxious for a child? How could any child be worth this suffering? What sense was there in making a helpless infant at the cost of so young a life as Ariel's? What a miserable absurdity it was, this business of reproducing the race,—to rear a girl through years and years of patient care, to make her happy and healthy, and then to sacrifice her, as if to another Moloch, on the altar of the species! And what was the species itself but millions of mothers suffering so, and millions of men standing by them, as I stood now by Ariel, guilty and helpless?

When Dr. Telfaer came I was again asked to step aside; but from my chair in the waiting-room I could hear them debating the advisability of an operation. Dr. Telfaer opposed it.

"Wait a little," he said. "Wait till noon."

It was seven o'clock now, and Ariel's family, called by me over the telephone, came to see her. First Harry, always cheerful, and refusing to believe that there was any real danger; what a comfort he was to me during those days! And then Morris and Flora and Mary and Michael, full of tender anxiety, but all confident that Ariel's health and strength would see her through. And finally the mother, gentle and timid, and already in tears as she entered the room. We went to where Ariel was sleeping, her face red and swollen.

"Don't wake her, mother," I whispered.

She longed to hear her daughter's voice, but she said nothing. She wanted to embrace her, but she held herself back. Instead, she went behind the head of the bed, bent down, and kissed again and again

Ariel's dishevelled hair, that streamed over the pillow. Then we drew her away.

"My Khaya, my Khaya," she cried, quietly.

I knew that she was thinking as I had thought: that she had borne this daughter with pain, and brought her up for many years through a thousand hardships, and lavished infinite love upon her,—for this, that she should die, perhaps, in the effort to bring into the world another child fated to similar suffering and similar futility. I could hardly look into her eyes; I felt responsible for this evil, and my shame made me almost wordless.

"Mother," I said, "if Ariel does not live I won't either."

She shook her head sadly.

"No, John," she whispered, "you mustn't say that. It isn't your fault."

I owe them all a great debt for their gentleness to me that morning. The cruel chasm of race had once divided us, and yet they held me now as a brother. Harry above all was kind, and stayed with me throughout that anxious Sunday, and through my two sleepless nights, never leaving me till the end.

At one o'clock the physicians were again in conference. Dr. Cox came into the waiting-room and said:

"No operation yet. We'll wait a few hours longer. She may be strong enough to have a natural delivery."

All this time Ariel slept; and so deeply that every now and then I went in, on tiptoe, to assure myself that she was not dead. Three o'clock came, and yet she slept. Five o'clock came, the hour at which I was to address an audience at the Workers' Church; indifferently I saw the time come and pass; what were lectures to me now? Night came, and Ariel slept it through.

Late that Sunday evening the nurses wheeled a bed, on which a pale, emaciated mother lay, into the room opposite that in which Harry and I were sitting.

"Who is it?" I asked Dr. Nelson.

"The other eclampsia case," he answered reluctantly. "We operated on her this afternoon."

"Will she live?" I asked.

"We hope for the best," he answered. I knew that that was a medical formula for hope run dry.

I sat at the window, looking out into the dark, while Harry slept with his head on the table. I vowed never again to indulge in the pride of paternity. I remembered Ariel's hesitation, and my yearning; what an ignorant criminal I had been to forget, in all my arguments, that no human life is made without risking human life! What should I do if Ariel died?

"If Ariel dies," I thought, "I'll go far out into the woods and lie down on my face in the grass; and I'll never get up again."

I heard a commotion near the door, and went out.

Several nurses were gathered about the woman who had had the Cæsarian operation; and in the corridor the doctors were talking quietly.

"She's dying," said one of them, calmly.

"Yes," said another.

As I stepped out of the waiting room I could hear the woman's breathing,—quick, struggling gasps. Her eyes were closed, but her lips opened and trembled convulsively. Even as I looked at her through the door of her room her breathing became heavier, and a queer noise came from her throat.

"It's the death-rattle," said Dr. Cox. "Could you," he asked me, "call up her husband and ask him to come at once? Here's his card."

I took the card and went down stairs to the telephone. I heard the husband's voice, and stumbled for words.

"Come at once," I repeated.

"Is she dying? Tell me the truth," he pleaded.

"I don't know," I lied. "Come."

When I returned upstairs the woman was dead. The nurses had covered her face, and now they left and closed the door upon her.

I went back to the waiting room, and tried to sleep. A few minutes later the husband came, a handsome and passionate young man who knelt beside his dead wife and moaned all through the night. They showed him his motherless child, but he turned away from it blindly.

I could not sleep. In the stillness and the darkness

I heard the death-rattle of the young mother, just one year married; and saw my Ariel, too, lying like her, dead. Monday's sun was rising when I fell asleep, my head on the table at Harry's side.

Two hours later a sharp cry pierced my dulled senses.

"Jack! Jack! I want Jack!"

I stumbled out of the room and found my way to Ariel. She was reclining on her elbow, one hand pressing on her side, a look of pain and fear on her face. A nurse stood near her, but seemed to attach no importance to her cries and her suffering.

"Her pains are beginning," she said, simply.

"Beginning?" I muttered. So all these thirty hours since that first hammer-blow on the brain,—they were painless by comparison with what was coming? I took Ariel's hand, and spoke to her, but she did not know me.

"Jack! Jack!" she cried again, looking vaguely past me. "Where are you? Come to me! Oh, I'm going to die!"

Suddenly she raised her shoulders from the bed, opened her mouth wide for the breath that would hardly come, and moaned:

"O God! O God! O God!"

I put my arm around her neck and kissed her; but she did not notice me. Her face was white with torture, and her eyes, though open, seemed to see nothing but some ghastly vision of suffering and death, from which she wished to flee but could not. The nurse looked at her watch, and wrote something on a pad. Dr. Cox entered, and greeted us.

"How is she getting along?" he asked.

"She's been having pains at twenty-minute intervals," answered the nurse.

At that moment another woman in the ward began to cry out.

"I suppose I'd better go to her for a while," said the nurse, wearily. "Could you," she asked me, "time your wife's pains for half an hour or so?"

Her assumption that the pains would go on for more than half an hour filled me with rage against this irrational universe. My hand trembled as I took the pad.

"Dr. Cox," I said, "you should let every husband see his wife go through this. He would be a little kinder to her for a while."

"We can't afford to let them see it," he replied. "They might never have children again."

"Well," I said, bitterly, "is it worth the suffering?"

"It will be all over in an hour," he said, "and then you'll be more cheerful. You think it's nature's fault, but it's really our own. We turn our women into dolls, choose them for their slim waists, send them into factories, feed them on delicacies, and in general make pretty wrecks of them. Peasant women don't suffer so. In this case it's the result of one doctor's negligence.—Can you take care of the time-chart? Call me when the pains come at five-minute intervals."

I agreed, and he left us. While we talked Ariel slept, breathing always with difficulty. The Doctor had hardly gone when she lifted herself again on her side, her face drawn taut with pain.

"O mother!" she gasped, "O mother! O God!"

I stood there helpless. If I touched her she released herself from me; if I spoke her name, or mine, she did not seem to hear me. She was alone in her suffering. I noted the minute at which the pain had come, while the inevitable tears fell hot upon my hand.

Now the spasms became more frequent, and more severe. I seemed dulled by my consciousness of impotence; and as if in a trance I wrote on the pad, and looked at my watch. As I wrote, two other women, caught in the throes of procreation, sent their shrill shrieks through the room. I felt Dr. Cox's touch on my arm; he took the pad and the pencil from me, and without a word led me to my seat in the waiting room. I had wanted to see it all, to see every bit of this tragedy with which life's comedy begins; now I made no resistance and offered no word as I was led away. But I kept whispering to myself, incoherently:

"I must always be kind to women. I must always be kind to women."

An hour later the child had been born, and Ariel, though still breathing heavily, was silent and still. I bent over her.

"Ariel," I said, "this is Jack. Do you know me? I shall always be good to you."

I think she did not hear me. She turned round with a sigh, moaned for a while, and then fell asleep. I sat by her a long time, grateful that she could sleep at last, and that she had come up from the battlefield where life is won. She was dearer to me now than ever before; dear with a love too deep for any words, and lifted far beyond the passing hunger of the flesh. I knew that she had paid a terrible price for the child she had given me. Dr. Cox entered, and asked would I come and see my little daughter; she was washed and dressed now, and fit for company. But I was absolutely apathetic.

"I don't care to see her yet," I said dully.

He smiled, and left me alone.

A moment later a specialist came and examined Ariel's eyes. They were insensitive to even a bright light placed close before them.

"Will her sight come back?" I asked, almost too weakly to be heard.

"I think so," the doctor replied.

I had to be content with that.

Throughout the day Ariel slept. In the afternoon Dr. Cox took me into a large, darkened room, that had almost the temperature of a hot-house. Here in their baskets were the new-born babes. Some were covered with blotches, others were drooling at the mouth; some had great red marks on their temples, where the forceps had taken hold to pull them, willy-nilly, into the world. Some were awake and crying; others moved restlessly in their sleep. We stopped before a baby that seemed to me cleaner and plumper than the rest.

"This is your little girl," said Dr. Cox. "What are you going to call her?"

I was not ready with the answer.

"We thought it would be a boy," I said.

"Never mind," he smiled. "A girl is much more affectionate. Some day you'll love her more than you could ever have loved a boy."

That evening I went out to lecture, drunk with sleeplessness and harassed with the vision of a permanently blinded Ariel. When the talk was over, friends inquired why I had dragged physicians, hospitals, medicines, forceps, and Cæsarian operations into a lecture on philosophy. I begged for mercy; and in my explanations I discerned already a trace of insane pride in having reproduced my species, however weakly.

That night I slept at home with Harry. Early the next morning I hurried to the hospital and Ariel's side. She was awake, after a sleep of twenty hours.

"Jack!" she cried; "I knew you'd come early."

"Darling," I said, covering her with kisses; "can you see me?"

"See you? Of course. Why do you ask that?"

"Yesterday, sweetheart, you were blind."

"Blind?"

"Yes; don't you remember?"

"No," she said, wondering.

"Don't you remember the doctor examining your eyes?"

"No. Did he?"

"Do you remember how they took you to the hospital?"

"No."

"Don't you remember the convulsions, or the pains?"

"I remember the headache. But did I have convulsions?"

I passed to other topics. It was well that she could not remember.

"Have they shown you our baby, Ariel?" I asked.

"Yes. When they told me it was a girl I cried. But when they showed her to me I fell in love with her. She's such a pretty baby, Jack."

I was comforted to see that Ariel was returning to life and normal reactions.

"Nurse," she said, "isn't it time to give her a little food?"

"Not yet," said the nurse.

"Ah, won't you bring her anyway, and let her daddy see her?"

"It's against the rules," the nurse answered.

But she went out, and soon came back with a bundle, and presented it to Ariel. Why is it that at once I loved that little bundle profoundly, and raised the coverings with the tenderest care? Instinctively I felt that this queer wriggling baby was to be infinitely precious to me. I knew that a million such tots came into the world every day, and were dear beyond utterance to one mother and one father, and seemed to them incomparably beautiful. But I was comfortably like others; I was sure that I had never seen so fair an infant face before.

"She will be pretty," I said, fondly.

"Let me have her," said Ariel, smiling through her tears.

And as the baby clutched at her breast, and finding its food, nestled contentedly against her warm body, she looked down at it tenderly.

"I'm so happy it's over, Jack," she said.

"Will you ever forgive me, sweetheart?" I asked.

She held her arm out to me and drew my cheek down against hers.

"I'm glad she came," she whispered. "Isn't she sweet?"

I sat beside her many hours, listening to her lovingly. I could have knelt and kissed the earth.

CHAPTER XIV

ENTSAGEN

It is right that my story should end here; for since Ethel came my world has revolved about her rather than about me, and I have had the happiness of the nation that knows no history. I should never have expected to be so easily content, and to resign so readily my ambition to remake the world. It astonishes me when I reflect how one breath of creation turned the current of my life and wafted my little bark to port. I can hardly express the change in words; and though I shall try, I know that I shall not be able to tell how happy I am, and why. It is all so unreasonable, and all so natural.

Do you remember, Ariel, how solicitous we were of our precious tot when finally they let you go from the hospital, and we were in our home again? How carefully we laid her in the big crib that our friends had sent us, how we placed the crib alongside our bed at night, and moved always inaudibly lest the babe should lose one wink of sleep? How content you were to be aroused from your slumber by its little voice, and to give your breast to her searching mouth! Why were we so happy? Was it because we had at last surrendered to nature, and she had filled our souls with the music of parental love?

For a time it was difficult for me to realize that there were other children in the world. When I brought Ethel down to her carriage at the door, and saw other infants there, I wondered how their mothers could be so enthusiastic over those puny wriggling legs, those dull eyes in those bulging heads. I struggled to utter the hypocritical compliments that were expected of me; but when the compliments were returned in the spirit in which they had been given, I accepted them as sincere and unavoidable admissions that Ethel's beauty was quite without parallel in the history of mankind. Proudly I took Ariel's place, on many an afternoon, and perambulated through streets and parks with the little princess in the carriage before me. And when it was Ariel's turn, and she had come back from her walk, she would give the door-bell a mystic ring which meant that I must come down and carry our plump and rosy heiress up the stairs to our rooms. I used to kiss my burden at every one of those hundred steps.

Ariel and I were united now as we had never been before. We felt, without putting it into words, that we had passed from mating into marriage. We labored for our little fraction of the future as if she were half the human race. We had always argued against the inheritance of property, as adding an artificial injustice to the superabundant inequalities which nature had established among men; but now, without ever stopping to refute our forgotten arguments, we began to stint and save, just as our parents had done before us, to give our child a better body and a better mind than ours, and to leave to her, when we died, some security against the accidents of life. We behaved as if we had never heard of Marx, and were normal members of the human species. It dawned upon us that the family was more important than the state, that man had become man through parental love, and that nature was right in turning our eyes from the problems of the universe to the needs of our little home. We had found our place, and were content; in the fulfilment of function we had discovered happiness.

"But don't you think it's selfish of us to be happy this way?" Ariel said, as we bent together over Ethel's crib and watched her in her sleep. "Think of the millions of people who are unhappy."

"Perhaps," I suggested, hopefully, "they too will learn the secret. Perhaps they too will find Ariels and Ethels."

"But there's so much disease, and ignorance, and bad temper in the world, so much greed and lust and violence. Shan't we ever get rid of them?"

"Once," I said, "we were all brutes. Do you think, Ariel, that there were souls like Jesus, or St. Francis, or Spinoza, or Raphael, among the cave men? Or minds like Plato's or Leonardo's, or Goethe's? Our violence may be a relic of the hunting stage; we are leaving it behind us as we grow."

She smiled.

"I'm so glad you're learning to hope again," she said.

Yes, I was relearning hope. I had demanded too much of my country and my race. Unconsciously I had been comparing the average of my time and place with the selected best of all past peoples and all the generations. I had complained because our philosophers were not like Aristotle, nor our painters like Rembrandt, nor our poets like Shakespeare, nor our composers like Bach. It had slipped my little mind that these lights had not all shone in the same sky.

And I had forgotten that America was young; that its virgin soil had naturally called the most individualistic and adventurous of Europe's sons, not those timid souls in whom art and letters find their continuity. These subtler minds would come to us later, when we had put our house in order. Wealth such as men had never known was multiplying in these States, and was scattering schools and universities and libraries and museums through the land. Would it all be useless? Would bigotry and intolerance darken again the opening mind of America? No; knowledge would grow from more to more, and would conquer inch by inch the strongholds of ignorance. In another century there would be more enlightenment in America than ever in the history of mankind. America had been a nation for but a century and a half; what would she not do in her maturity? What wealth would she not produce, and what genius?—I began to look again with a forgiving eye upon the sins of my country, its provincial narrowness of mind, its worship of material possessions and display, its crimes against the growth and freedom of the soul. These things would pass away.

Why hope should have this second blooming in my heart I cannot say, except that it came spontaneously with my unreasonable happiness. When I looked at Ethel sleeping, her calm and ruddy face illumined by the moon that seemed to bend from the clouds to caress her, I felt that in such cradles everywhere, rather than in complicated political or economic schemes, lay the future of America. Surely it would be a finer generation than ours, dowered with instrumentalities of growth and culture such as our youth had never known. Those men and women who were to come out of our chaos and uncertainty would be raised on the shoulders of our suffering, and would see with clearer eyes than ours the nobility of freedom and the beauty of peace. Through my own little girl I saw her million growing comrades, children of this new century, unsullied by our wars, uplifted by our care, facing the future with fresh hope, and opening new paths to that ever-promised land which we too had seen, but which we had lost forever because we had stained our hands with blood.

It is strange, and perhaps ridiculous, that these simple events subtly affected my philosophy. Even before Ethel's coming I had begun to rebel against that mechanical conception of mind and history which is the illegitimate offspring of our industrial age; I had suspected that the old agricultural view of the world in terms of seed and growth did far more justice to the complexity and irrepressible expansiveness of things. But when Ethel came, and I saw how some mysterious inner impulse, far outreaching the categories of physics, lifted her up, inch by inch and effort by effort, on the ladder of life, I felt more keenly than before the need of a philosophy that would do justice to the infinite vitality of nature. In the inexhaustible activity of the atom, in the endless resourcefulness of plants, in the teeming fertility of animals, in the hunger and movement of infants, in the laughter and play of children, in the love and devotion of youth, in the restless ambition of fathers and the life-long sacrifice of mothers, in the undiscourageable researches of scientists and the sufferings of genius, in the crucifixion of prophets and the martyrdom of saints,—in all things I saw the passion of life for growth and greatness, the drama of everlasting creation. I came to think of myself not as a dance and chaos of molecules, but as a brief and minute portion of that majestic process, burning with the impulse to create, to capture truth and fashion beauty, and to leave behind me something better than myself. I became almost reconciled to mortality, knowing that my spirit would survive me enshrined in a fairer mould than mine, and that my little worth would somehow be preserved in the heritage of men. In a measure the Great Sadness was lifted from me; and where I had seen omnipresent death I saw now everywhere about me the pageant and triumph of life.

Every morning Ethel wakes me with the touch of her little hand upon my face; every day I work to the tune of her laughter and her song.

It was Ethel who found a way back for me into my father's heart. She knew no theology, and smiled as radiantly upon him as if the barriers of race and faith meant even less to her clear soul than to the wisest sage. He had come with my mother to see us in our Fordham home; it was a gracious symbol of forgiveness in them to make so long a trip despite their three-score years and ten. When, in July, my father's seventieth year was coming to an end, Ariel and Ethel and I returned that visit gladly, and shared in the birthday celebration with half a hundred reunited members of the family. I had missed these festivals through the days of our separation; and when the night came on which I knew that my brothers and sisters and their children had gathered to do honor to their parents, I spent unhappy hours in lonely meditation. But now we sat again at the same table, under the old-fashioned chandelier, in the old home of my youth; again my father, gray but strong, presided gladly over the two generations of his children; and my mother, white-haired but beautiful, waited on us fondly, overwhelming us with luxuries. And when she laid before my father an enormous apple pie, proud product of her perfect art, she put her sturdy arms around his neck and said to us, with splendid passion:

"I thank God for giving me this dear old man to take care of me these seventy years."

Then I heard my brothers urging me to make a speech, to express something of what we felt towards the tenderest of mothers and the kindliest of fathers. Was I not a professional speech-maker? Of what use was all my training if I could not phrase their devotion now? I refused; I knew that I could not go through with it. But they gathered around me merrily, forced me to my feet, and vowed they would never let me free until I spoke for them. I tried.

"I'm so glad," I began, "that we're all together once more."

Then the old sentimental tears came and blinded me, and a rising tide of feeling swept my thoughts away. I sat down in helpless confusion; but my father, equal to the occasion, raised us all to our feet with a toast that gave simple expression to the hope in all our hearts:

"May we never be separated again."

And now we are in "Utopia." It is no imagined paradise of coming centuries, but a pleasant place among the hills of this imperfect and contemporary earth. As I sit and write I am surrounded by a hundred thousand pine-trees, eternally fragrant and green. Here and there, almost lost among the spreading branches, are the bungalows of the girls. Pretty girls, almost every one of them; I did not know the world had so many. On the level below I see the boys playing tennis; their wet brown shoulders gleam in the sun; their voices make in the distance the music of persistent life. Farther off I see the lake, nestling quietly in the lap of the hills; and I know that Ethel is frolicking there.

Here she is now coming back, dripping, skipping and laughing, her hair leaping with every toss of her head. She has been in the water for three hours, and yet is not exhausted; she must run to Ariel and then challenge her to a race up the lawn to me. Fondly Ariel lets her win, and she falls into my arms all wet and happy.

"O dad," she cries, "I learned a new stroke to-day. You ought to see me swim now."

What energy! What life! I see that my youth is not gone, it has only been reborn. Surely all things will be possible to man if time is generous.

Ethel is playing with Ariel out on the grass before me, singing. I cannot write any more; I must watch them. She sees me looking up, and takes advantage.

"Daddy, aren't you through with that old book yet?"

"Nearly through, Ethel."

"Come and play with us."

I exact a bribe.

"Do you love me?"

"More than the world." She holds out her chubby arms as if to span the universe. "Even when you scold me I love you."

I close my book, and bid you good fortune, dear Reader. I must go down there and play with Ethel and Ariel.

THE END